RYA/MCA Certificates of Competence

RYA/MCA Examinations

A Certificate of Competence signifies that the candidate has successfully passed an independent examination conducted by an RYA/MCA-appointed examiner.

RYA/MCA
Yachtmaster
Coastal (page 68)

RYA/MCA
Yachtmaster
Offshore (page 69)

RYA/MCA
Yachtmaster
Ocean (page 71)

Key to Courses

Motor
These courses form part of the RYA Yachtmaster
Scheme for motor-cruising boaters.

Sail
These courses form part of the RYA Yachtmaster
Scheme for sail-cruising boaters.

One Day
These courses are part of the RYA Shorebased
course scheme and can be taken in one day.

RYA Yachtmaster® Scheme Syllabus & Logbook

© RYA 2015
Reprinted July 2015
Updated March 2016
Updated January 2017, May 2017,
November 2017, June 2018, November 2018
The Royal Yachting Association
RYA House, Ensign Way,
Hamble, Southampton,
Hampshire SO31 4YA
Tel: 02380 604 100
Web: www.rya.org.uk
Follow us on Twitter @RYAPublications
or on YouTube

We welcome feedback on our publications at
publications@rya.org.uk

You can check content updates for RYA
publications at www.rya.org.uk/go/
bookschangelog

ISBN: 978-1-910017074
RYA Order Code: G158

A CIP record of this book is available from the
British Library.

Note: While all reasonable care has been taken
in the preparation of this book, the publisher
takes no responsibility for the use of the methods
or products or contracts described in this book.

Cover design: Pete Galvin
Typesetting and design: Velveo Design
Photographs: Paul Wyeth, RYA
Proofreading: Rob Melotti

Printed in China through World Print

Contents

Introduction

Finding the Right Course for you

Before taking a course you should look carefully at the experience requirement and, if necessary, discuss your level of ability with an RYA Training Centre. The intention of the courses is to improve your knowledge and skills and therefore allow you to gain more enjoyment from cruising. Attempting a course significantly above your current level will be counter-productive and we strongly recommend that you seek guidance from an RYA Training Centre as to the best course for you given your previous experience.

RYA Courses

RYA Theory and Practical courses are run by over 2,500 RYA Training Centres worldwide. To find an RYA Training Centre that will meet your needs, visit the RYA website (www.rya.org.uk) for a list of centres.

Shorebased

The Shorebased scheme teaches the theory of navigation and seamanship in courses of 16 or 40 hours' duration, plus home study. In some cases Theory courses can be delivered in an online format or combined in an online and classroom course. There are also one-day courses for the theory and practice of VHF radio operation, first aid, radar, sea survival, offshore safety, professional responsibilities, and diesel engine maintenance. See page 92 for more information.

Practical Courses

Practical courses take place at sea on board a cruising yacht or motor-cruising vessel operated by an RYA Training Centre. These are structured to provide specific courses from Start Yachting/Start Motor Cruising up to Coastal Skipper. See page 9 for more information.

Course Completion Certificates

Upon successful completion of all of the elements of your course the Principal or Chief Instructor will award you a course completion certificate.

The RYA/MCA Yachtmaster Scheme

RYA/MCA Yachtmaster Coastal and RYA Yachtmaster Offshore qualifications are achieved through the successful completion of an independent RYA/MCA practical examination. There is no requirement to take an RYA course before taking one of the examinations; however, you will need to ensure you possess the required standard of theory and practical ability highlighted on pages 61–78. The examinations are open to anyone with the required experience, provided they meet all of the prerequisite requirements.

Successful candidates will be awarded an appropriate Certificate of Competence (CoC). See page 61 for more information.

Certificates of Competence

An RYA/MCA Certificate of Competence is recognised by maritime authorities around the world and is in many countries the required qualification for professional skippers on small commercial vessels.

Keeping a Log

We recommend that you keep a record of your seatime. A validated record of your cruising experience is a useful indicator for the Practical courses and absolutely essential to enter for the RYA/MCA Yachtmaster examinations. This book provides log pages for you to fill in on pages 47–59 together with notes about experience and skill levels.

RYA Training Centres

All RYA Training Centres, which may be clubs, sailing schools or sea training organisations, should display a Certificate of Recognition specifying the activities for which they are recognised.

Recognition involves the school being run by an RYA Yachtmaster Instructor, all Instructors holding appropriate RYA Instructor qualifications and the vessels used conforming to regulations laid down by the National Maritime Authority of the country and the RYA. Centres are also required to carry public liability insurance and have appropriate safety procedures in place.

Safety is the top priority for the RYA. Each RYA Training Centre is regularly inspected for standards of tuition, facilities and equipment as set down by the RYA Training Department.

Learning Resources

The RYA produces a wide range of resources to help you learn:

- Course notes and exercises, comprehensive handbooks and topic books in both traditional and e-book formats
- Interactive training downloads for electronic plotting, navigation and seamanship theory
- A wide range of supporting DVDs.

All of these can be obtained through RYA Training Centres or the RYA webshop (www.rya.org.uk/shop).

Practical Courses up to Day Skipper

These courses are run over a minimum period of practical training, and successful completion will result in the award of a course completion certificate.

Members of the Association of Sail Training Organisations may deliver the training over a longer period.

All Practical certificates or Practical course completion certificates may be awarded irrespective of whether the candidate holds a certificate for the equivalent Shorebased course. However, in all cases the candidate must meet the prerequisites for the course. Students who have previously completed the relevant Shorebased course will find that their experience on the Practical course will be greatly enhanced as a result.

It is unlikely that students who do not have the equivalent level of Theory knowledge will achieve the standard required to pass the Practical course.

Advanced Pilotage and Coastal Skipper

It is assumed that candidates attending these courses will be competent boaters with a good knowledge of meteorology and the theory of navigation, and will already have over 10 days of experience, two days of which have been as skipper.

There is insufficient time during the course to teach the basic skills of seamanship, helmsmanship and navigation, as well as how these skills should be applied by the skipper of a cruising vessel.

Non-Tidal Courses

These courses are specifically designed for those who wish to sail in areas such as the Mediterranean, the Baltic and parts of the Caribbean. The courses are delivered at non-tidal RYA Training Centres. The majority of skills are the same, with the differences becoming apparent when manoeuvring in tide.

Courses below Day Skipper Level

Courses below the level of Day Skipper are the same in tidal and non-tidal waters. To convert a Non-Tidal certificate to Tidal, students can attend a two-day conversion course at a school recognised to issue Tidal certificates. Students should have a theoretical knowledge to the standard of the Day Skipper or Coastal Skipper Shorebased courses. Some students may require more than two days to achieve the Tidal conversion. A Tidal certificate will be issued on successful completion of the conversion.

Practical Training for the RYA/MCA Yachtmaster Offshore Certificate of Competence

No syllabus is prescribed for a Practical course for the RYA Yachtmaster Offshore Certificate. The reason for this is that the RYA/MCA Yachtmaster Certificates of Competence (Coastal, Offshore and Ocean) are awarded only after the successful completion of the relevant exam. There is no one course aimed at teaching this entire syllabus. Rather, candidates should attempt this exam only after having accrued at minimum the prerequisite mileage, experience and supplementary qualifications.

However, RYA Training Centres may offer courses in preparation for this examination, either to give candidates experience of making longer passages or simply as a refresher course on aspects of boat handling, navigation and seamanship. This course may only be run by a RYA Yachtmaster Instructor.

The exam syllabus is included on pages 74–76. However, it is important to note that any element of each course syllabus within the RYA Yachtmaster Scheme is within the scope for the examination.

Swimmers

It is strongly recommended that all those participating in the sport of cruising should be able to swim. Non-swimmers will normally be required to wear a life jacket at all times.

RYA
Practical Courses

The Syllabuses

The following pages describe the syllabus for each level of the RYA Yachtmaster Scheme. Due to time constraints and variations in course locations and equipment, not all subjects can be covered in great detail or practically on the water. We have therefore specified three levels of teaching to indicate the depth to which you can expect each item to be covered.

These levels are:

KNOWLEDGE OF the subject

The subject will be briefly explained. Familiarisation will occur during the course and information on where to find out more will be given.

UNDERSTANDS the subject

The subject will be covered in greater depth. You will be asked to demonstrate a basic understanding and go away from the course able to develop further your own skill in this area. Confirmation of your understanding of the subject may be achieved in a number of ways during the course.

CAN demonstrate a level of proficiency in the subject

The subject will be covered in great depth, including background theory, practical demonstrations by the Instructor and repeated practice by yourself until you can demonstrate a sound level of proficiency in the skill and/or knowledge of the subject.

Sailing Skills: Start Sailing – Level 1

This course provides a short introduction to sailing for novices. By the end of the course you will have a basic understanding of yacht handling under sail, including practical techniques and background knowledge. It is recommended that all participants consolidate this short introduction with the Basic Skills course.

Duration: Approximately 16 hours (either spread over a series of sessions or 2 full days).

Recommended minimum age: 12

Non-residential course.

Practical

1 Rigging

KNOWLEDGE OF:

- Spars and rigging; parts of the sail and sail controls
- Wind awareness ashore

UNDERSTANDS:

- Use of halyards and their associated winches

Instructor's signature _____ Date _____

2 Sailing Techniques and Manoeuvres

KNOWLEDGE OF:

- The Four Essentials (sail setting; balance; boat trim; course made good)

UNDERSTANDS:

- Wind awareness afloat
- Sailing upwind
- Controlling speed
- Sailing downwind
- Tacking – turning the front of the boat through the wind
- Gybing – turning the back of the boat through the wind, from a training run
- The importance of good communication when manoeuvring

CAN:

- Reach – sailing across the wind
- Stop – heave-to

Instructor's signature _____ Date _____

Recommended pre-course experience:			
Days at sea:	0	Night Hours:	0
Miles:	0	Days as Skipper:	0

3 Slipping and Coming Alongside

KNOWLEDGE OF:

- The action to be taken as a crew member when departing or arriving at the yacht's mooring

Instructor's signature _____ Date _____

4 Ropework

KNOWLEDGE OF:

- Round turn and two half hitches; clove hitch; bowline

CAN:

- Tie a figure of eight knot; secure a rope to a cleat; secure a fender to the yacht

Instructor's signature _____ Date _____

5 Clothing and Equipment

CAN:

- Use and correctly fit life jackets
- Use a safety harness if fitted

Instructor's signature _____ Date _____

6 Emergency Equipment and Precautions

KNOWLEDGE OF:

- How cold-water shock can affect a casualty in the water

UNDERSTANDS:

- The potential hazards of fuel and gas
- Where safety equipment is stowed and how it is used

CAN:

- Perform actions to be taken as a crew member to recover a man overboard (MOB)

Instructor's signature _____ Date _____

Sailing Theory

1 Clothing and Equipment

KNOWLEDGE OF:

* The importance of personal safety, clothing and buoyancy

Instructor's signature _____   Date _____

2 Sailing Background

KNOWLEDGE OF:

* How to be aware of other water users
* Basic rules of the road – collision avoidance; power/sail; port/starboard; overtaking boat; windward boat

CAN:

* Use visual methods to attract attention

Instructor's signature _____   Date _____

3 Meteorology

KNOWLEDGE OF:

* Where to obtain a weather forecast

Instructor's signature _____   Date _____

Sailing Skills: Basic Skills – Level 2

On completion of this course you will have a basic knowledge of sailing and be capable of sailing a yacht in light winds as crew and helm with a skipper on board. It will be assumed that every student starting this course has already mastered the practical skills and absorbed the background knowledge required for Start Sailing – Level 1. Both courses can be combined, which will then count towards two days of a Competent Crew course.

Duration: Approximately 16 hours (either spread over a series of sessions or 2 full days).

Recommended minimum age: 12

Non-residential course.

Practical

1 Rigging

CAN:

- Rig according to weather conditions
- Reef alongside

Instructor's signature _____   Date _____

2 Sailing Techniques and Manoeuvres

KNOWLEDGE OF:

- Leaving and returning to a jetty or mooring
- Coming alongside a moored boat
- Sailing in close proximity to other vessels
- Performing a man-overboard recovery
- Lee shore dangers

UNDERSTANDS:

- Sailing using transits

CAN:

- Use the Four Essentials (sail setting; balance; boat trim; course made good)
- Tack while sailing upwind, sailing efficiently, losing minimal ground
- Gybe in a controlled manner while sailing downwind
- Show good communication when manoeuvring
- Show awareness of other water users
- Sail around a short course using all points of sail and crewing skills
- Anchor

Instructor's signature _____   Date _____

Recommended pre-course experience:			
Days at sea:	2	Night Hours:	0
Miles:	0	Days as Skipper:	0

3 Ropework

CAN:

* Tie a bowline, clove hitch and reef knot

Instructor's signature _____ Date _____

4 Racing

KNOWLEDGE OF:

* The course and starting procedure (covered as onshore session)

Instructor's signature _____ Date _____

5 Rigging

CAN:

* Reef afloat

Instructor's signature _____ Date _____

6 Ropework

CAN:

* Use winches and cleats

Instructor's signature _____ Date _____

7 Use of Engines

KNOWLEDGE OF:

* Engine checks; starting, stopping and running procedures
* Picking up a mooring

UNDERSTANDS:

* Coming alongside

Instructor's signature _____ Date _____

8 Emergency Equipment and Precautions

KNOWLEDGE OF:

- A VHF radio and how it could be used for distress signalling

UNDERSTANDS:

- How to launch and board a life raft
- How cold-water shock can affect a casualty in the water
- The importance of first aid kits and flares, including stowage

Instructor's signature   Date

Sailing Theory

1 Clothing and Equipment

UNDERSTANDS:

- The importance of personal safety

CAN:

- Comply with rules for the wearing of safety harnesses, life jackets and personal buoyancy aids

Instructor's signature   Date

2 Slipping and Coming Alongside

CAN:

- Take the action required as a crew member when departing or arriving at the yacht's mooring

Instructor's signature   Date

3 Sailing Background

KNOWLEDGE OF:

- How a sail works
- How a sailing boat moves (basic theory)

UNDERSTANDS:

- Basic rules of the road; collision avoidance; power/sail; port/starboard; windward boat; overtaking boat
- The points of sailing and the 'no go zone'

Instructor's signature   Date

4 Meteorology

KNOWLEDGE OF:

- The Beaufort Wind Scale
- Inshore forecasts and their interpretation
- A simple synoptic chart

UNDERSTANDS:

- Sources of relevant weather forecasts
- When to reef

Instructor's signature _____ Date _____

Coastal Waters

KNOWLEDGE OF:

- Tide tables

UNDERSTANDS:

- How to apply weather forecasts in coastal waters
- The tidal sequence of springs and neaps, and ebb and flow
- Speed over ground with/against tidal flow
- The effect of wind direction and tidal flow on sailing conditions
- How to access local information and advice for sea sailing
- The importance of informing someone ashore of your sailing plan

Instructor's signature _____ Date _____

Start Yachting

This course provides a short introduction for novices to sail cruising. By the end of the course you will have experienced steering a yacht, sail handling, ropework, and be aware of safety on board.

Duration: Two days. Holders of a Start Yachting certificate can obtain a Competent Crew certificate by completing a further three days or two weekends of the Competent Crew course.

Recommended minimum age: 8

Residential course.

1 The Yacht

KNOWLEDGE OF:

* Sea terms; parts of a boat; her rigging and sails

Instructor's signature _____ Date _____

2 Ropework

UNDERSTANDS:

* The bowline

CAN:

* Tie the following knots: figure of eight; round turn and two half hitches
* Secure a rope to a cleat
* Use winches and jamming cleats

Instructor's signature _____ Date _____

3 Under Way

KNOWLEDGE OF:

* Sailing a yacht on all points of sail

CAN:

* Steer a yacht under sail or power

Instructor's signature _____ Date _____

Recommended pre-course experience:			
Days at sea:	0	Night Hours:	0
Miles:	0	Days as Skipper:	0

4 Rules of the Road

CAN:
- Keep an efficient lookout at sea

Instructor's signature _____ Date _____

5 Meteorology

UNDERSTANDS:
- Where to obtain a weather forecast

Instructor's signature _____ Date _____

6 Man Overboard Recovery

UNDERSTANDS:
- The action to be taken as crew to recover a man overboard
- The effects of cold-water shock on a casualty

Instructor's signature _____ Date _____

7 Clothing and Equipment

UNDERSTANDS:
- Good practice for the wearing of safety harnesses, life jackets and personal buoyancy aids

Instructor's signature _____ Date _____

8 Emergency Equipment and Precautions

UNDERSTANDS:
- Hazards on board a yacht
- Actions to be taken in the event of an emergency

Instructor's signature _____ Date _____

Start Motor Cruising

This course aims to introduce the skills required to be a useful crew member and you will gain an understanding of how you can assist the skipper.

Duration: One day as a stand-alone course, or two days when accompanying other courses.

Minimum age: 8.

Non-residential course.

1 Personal Safety

UNDERSTANDS:

- The difference between manual and auto-inflating life jackets
- The importance of crotch straps
- Appropriate clothing
- Cold shock

CAN:

- Correctly fit a life jacket

Instructor's signature _____ Date _____

2 Seamanship

UNDERSTANDS:

- The importance of securely storing items before going to sea

CAN:

- Keep a lookout

Instructor's signature _____ Date _____

Recommended pre-course experience:			
Days at sea:	0	Night Hours:	0
Miles:	0	Days as Skipper:	0

3 Emergency Situations

KNOWLEDGE OF:

- Problems that can happen at sea

UNDERSTANDS:

- Their role in an emergency
- How to raise the alarm
- How to prevent man overboard
- The safety procedures on their vessel

CAN:

- Deploy the anchor (8–11 year olds to observe this session only)
- Locate lifesaving appliances (LSAs) and first aid kit
- Read a position from the Global Navigation Satellite System (GNSS)
- Use a boat hook

Instructor's signature _____ Date _____

4 Coming Alongside/Picking up a Mooring

KNOWLEDGE OF:

- What the manoeuvre entails

UNDERSTANDS:

- Preparation of mooring lines
- Communication and the importance of letting the helm know when they have slipped or attached the lines

CAN:

- Attach fenders
- Coil a line
- Throw a mooring line
- Attach a line to a cleat

Instructor's signature _____ Date _____

5 Boat Handling

UNDERSTANDS:

- The importance of crew communication

CAN (under direction):

- Start and stop the engine
- Steer and control boat speed
- Pick up a mooring

Instructor's signature _____ Date _____

Helmsman's Course

This course aims to teach boat handling and seamanship in motor cruisers. By the end of the course you will feel comfortable berthing and unberthing in straightforward locations and should be confident in general boat handling.

Duration: Two days.

Minimum age: 12.

Non-residential/residential course.

Practical

1 Safety and Seamanship

UNDERSTANDS:

- The importance of crotch straps
- The difference between manual and auto-inflating life jackets
- Appropriate clothing

CAN:

- Correctly fit a life jacket

Instructor's signature _____ Date _____

2 Engine Operation and Maintenance

KNOWLEDGE OF:

- Fuel consumption range and reserve

UNDERSTANDS:

- Engine monitoring while running
- Routine maintenance checks
- Basic fault diagnosis

CAN:

- Perform pre-start checks
- Locate fuel cut-offs
- Perform close-down procedure

Instructor's signature _____ Date _____

Recommended pre-course experience:			
Days at sea:	0	Night Hours:	0
Miles:	0	Days as Skipper:	0

3 Boat Preparation

KNOWLEDGE OF:

- Local boating conditions and regulations
- CE marks; loading; effect on handling and performance

UNDERSTANDS:

- Safety equipment; life jackets; dangers; the need for crew
- Use of a kill cord (if fitted)
- Secure stowage of equipment

CAN:

- Tie and know the use of relevant knots: round turn and two half hitches; bowline; clove hitch
- Prepare boat, lines and fenders

Instructor's signature   Date

4 Boat Handling

KNOWLEDGE OF:

- Differences between hull shapes and propulsion systems

UNDERSTANDS:

- Steering; controls; windage
- The effect of wind on bow
- Carrying way
- Movement around the boat and crew positioning at sea
- Boat control in waves
- Use of power trim and trim tabs

CAN:

- Start and stop the engine
- Steer a straight course at low speed
- Turn in a confined space
- Handle a boat at planing speed
- Use trim tabs/power trim (where fitted)

Instructor's signature   Date

5 Securing to a Buoy

UNDERSTANDS:

- The importance of crew communication
- Methods of approach in various wind and tide conditions
- Taking way off
- The procedure when overshooting

CAN:

- Prepare mooring warps
- Use a boat hook
- Make fast
- Approach and secure to a buoy

Instructor's signature   Date

6 Berthing Alongside and Leaving

UNDERSTANDS:

- Preparation and use of lines and springs
- Methods of approach in various conditions

CAN:

- Attach fenders
- Coil a line
- Throw a mooring line
- Secure lines to cleats
- Make fast alongside
- Use springs to leave a berth

Instructor's signature   Date

7 Man Overboard

KNOWLEDGE OF:

- Various methods for recovering the person overboard from the water

UNDERSTANDS:

- That engines should be switched off unless it is unsafe to do so
- Drift-down approach

CAN:

- Take immediate action
- Observe the man overboard
- Carry out the correct return with awareness of the propellers
- Approach and recover the man-overboard dummy

Instructor's signature   Date

8 Anchoring

KNOWLEDGE OF:

- Types of anchor
- Depth of water; holding ground; scope required

UNDERSTANDS:

- Stowage and attachment to boat
- Preparation of anchor, chain and warp
- Correct approaches in various conditions
- Taking way off
- The importance of crew communication
- Use of windlass
- Weighing anchor

CAN:

- Approach and anchor
- Check holding
- Weigh anchor

Instructor's signature   Date

Theory

1 Vessel

KNOWLEDGE OF:

- Types of craft
- The advantages/disadvantages of different hull types with respect to seakeeping ability and wash considerations
- Engines and drives – advantages/disadvantages of different drive systems
- The choice and use of fuel

Instructor's signature   Date

Competent Crew

The Competent Crew course introduces the complete beginner to cruising. You will learn about personal safety, seamanship and helmsmanship to the level required to be a useful member of the crew of a cruising yacht.

Duration: Five days/three sets of two days/five days non-consecutively in sets of three days and two days.

Recommended minimum age: 12

Residential course.

1 Sea Terms and Parts of a Boat, her Rigging and Sails

UNDERSTANDS:

• Orders given concerning the sailing and day-to-day running of the boat

Instructor's signature _____   Date _____

2 Sail Handling

CAN:

• Bend on, set, reef and handle sails
• Use sheets and halyards and their associated winches

Instructor's signature _____   Date _____

3 Ropework

CAN:

• Use sheets and halyards and their associated winches
• Handle ropes, including coiling, stowing, securing to cleats and single and double bollards
• Handle warps
• Tie the following knots and knows their correct use: figure-of-eight; clove hitch; bowline; round turn and two half hitches; reef knot, rolling hitch, single and double sheet bend

Instructor's signature _____   Date _____

Recommended pre-course experience:			
Days at sea:	0	Night Hours:	0
Miles:	0	Days as Skipper:	0

4 Safety on Board

UNDERSTANDS:

* Fire precautions and fighting
  * What the particular hazards are, and actions to be taken to prevent and in the event of fire
* On-board alarms, including gas and carbon monoxide

Instructor's signature   Date

5 Personal Safety Equipment

UNDERSTANDS:

* How to comply with guidance for the wearing of safety harnesses, life jackets and personal buoyancy aids

Instructor's signature   Date

6 Man Overboard

UNDERSTANDS:

* The action to be taken to recover a man overboard
* How cold-water shock can affect a casualty in the water

Instructor's signature   Date

7 Emergency Equipment

UNDERSTANDS:

* How to launch and board a life raft
* Distress flares and knows when they should be used

Instructor's signature   Date

8 Manners and Customs

UNDERSTANDS:

* Accepted practice with regard to: use of burgees and ensigns; prevention of unnecessary noise or disturbance in harbour including courtesies to other berthed craft
* The responsibility of the boating community to protect the environment

Instructor's signature   Date

9 Rules of the Road

CAN:

* Keep an efficient lookout at sea

Instructor's signature _____ Date _____

10 Tender Usage

UNDERSTANDS:

* The loading rules and complies with them
* The use and importance of a kill cord
* Safety equipment for tenders

CAN:

* Handle a dinghy under oars

Instructor's signature _____ Date _____

11 Meteorology

KNOWLEDGE OF:

* The Beaufort Scale

UNDERSTANDS:

* The forecasting services and where to obtain a forecast

Instructor's signature _____ Date _____

12 Seasickness

* Working efficiency is unaffected/partially affected/severely affected by seasickness (Delete as applicable)

UNDERSTANDS:

* How to reduce the effects of seasickness (e.g. steer, look at the horizon, take anti-seasickness tablets before going afloat)

Instructor's signature _____ Date _____

13 Helmsmanship and Sailing

UNDERSTANDS:

* The basic principles of sailing

CAN:

* Steer and trim sails on all points of sailing
* Steer a compass course, under sail and power

Instructor's signature   Date

14 General Duties

CAN:

* Carry out general duties satisfactorily on deck and below decks in connection with the daily routine of the vessel

Instructor's signature   Date

Watch Leader

The Watch Leader course is conducted on board a large cruising vessel or a motor/sail training vessel (over 15m Length Overall (LOA)). You will learn about watchkeeping, seamanship and navigation up to the standards required for taking charge of a watch on deck, at sea or in harbour, under the supervision of a deck officer. The Watch Leader syllabus can be conducted in tidal or non-tidal waters.

Minimum duration: Five days.

The recommended minimum age for the award of the certificate is 14.

1 Preparation for Sea

KNOWLEDGE OF:

- Stability

CAN:

- Secure and stow all gear on deck and below
- Prepare crew
- Carry out engine, life-saving and firefighting apparatus checks
- Additional for Sail:
  - Steer and trim sails on all points of sailing

Instructor's signature *Sail*   *Motor*   Date

2 Deck Work

CAN:

- Organise a watch to carry out the following duties:
  - Prepare, drop and weigh anchor
  - Prepare, send and retrieve warps while coming to or slipping alongside
  - Mooring to and slipping from a buoy
- Additional for Sail:
  - Sail hoists and sail drops
  - Reefing and shaking out reefs

Instructor's signature *Sail*   *Motor*   Date

Recommended pre-course experience:			
Days at sea:	5	Night Hours:	4
Miles:	100	Days as Skipper:	0

3 Navigation

KNOWLEDGE OF:

- The uses and limitations of Automatic Identification System (AIS)

UNDERSTANDS:

- IALA buoyage
- Use of a lead line, or similar

CAN:

- Plot a fix using electronic means
- Maintain navigational records
- Use an echo sounder

Instructor's signature *Sail* _____ *Motor* _____ Date _____

4 Pilotage

UNDERSTANDS:

- The use of leading lines, clearing lines, transits, and soundings

Instructor's signature *Sail* _____ *Motor* _____ Date _____

5 Meteorology

UNDERSTANDS:

- Sources of forecast information

CAN:

- Record weather forecasts from radio broadcast sources

Instructor's signature *Sail* _____ *Motor* _____ Date _____

6 Rules of the Road

CAN:

- Demonstrate a practical understanding of the International Regulations for Preventing Collisions at Sea

Instructor's signature *Sail* _____ *Motor* _____ Date _____

7 Maintenance and Repair Work

UNDERSTANDS:

- The importance of using protective equipment and safe procedures when carrying out maintenance
- The use and properties of common synthetic rope
- Correct procedures for control, handling and disposal of hazardous substances

CAN:

- Carry out regular checks on all machinery and equipment as per manufacturers' specifications
- Identify chafe and wear & tear

Instructor's signature *Sail* _____ *Motor* _____ Date _____

8 Engines

Has a working knowledge of the prevention of common engine faults and is competent in the following areas:

UNDERSTANDS:

- The need for periodic maintenance checks on engines and electrical installations
- The requirements for tool kits, spares and lubricants
- The location of filters and bleed points for fuel
- The tension of drive belts and how to change them

CAN:

- Carry out checks before starting, while running and after stopping
- Clean water filters and knows the location of impellors
- Estimate fuel consumption at various speeds and knows the effects of fouling

Instructor's signature *Sail* _____ *Motor* _____ Date _____

9 Victualling

UNDERSTANDS:

- The principles of food hygiene
- How to victual and make provision for consumables such as water and gas

CAN:

- Monitor usage of victuals and freshness of perishables

Instructor's signature *Sail* _____ *Motor* _____ Date _____

10 Tender

UNDERSTANDS:

- Safety equipment for tenders
- Loading rules; launch and recovery

CAN:

- Safely operate a tender under power
- Use a kill cord at all times when under power

Instructor's signature *Sail*   *Motor*   Date

11 Emergency Situations

UNDERSTANDS:

- The correct action to take as watch leader during: fire, sinking, abandonment, or the recovery of an MOB
- How to operate all life-saving and firefighting appliances on board including: watertight doors; hatches and storm boards; life rafts, fire extinguishers, and distress flares
- Helicopter rescue procedure
- The effects of cold-water shock on a casualty in the water
- How to send a distress message by VHF/DSC

Instructor's signature *Sail*   *Motor*   Date

12 General Watchkeeping

CAN:

Carry out watch-leading duties while at sea or in harbour with respect to:

- Standing orders and watch bills
- Domestic duties
- The even apportioning of workload
- Maintenance of personal standards

Instructor's signature *Sail*   *Motor*   Date

Day Skipper

The Day Skipper course is taught on board a cruising yacht (for the Sail course) or motor cruiser (for the Motor course) of 7 metres Length of Waterline (LWL) to 15 metres (LOA). You will learn pilotage, navigation, seamanship and boat handling up to the standard required to skipper a small cruising yacht or motor cruiser safely by day in waters with which you are familiar.

Duration: Sail: Five days/three sets of two days/five days non-consecutively in sets of three days and two days. Motor: Four days/two groups of two days.

The minimum age for the award of the certificate is 16.

1 Preparation for Sea

1 Preparation for Sea

KNOWLEDGE OF:

* Basic stability and buoyancy for small vessels

CAN:

* Prepare a cruising vessel for sea, including engine checks, securing and stowage of all gear on deck and below

* Additional for Sail:
  * Selection of sails

Instructor's signature *Sail*   *Motor*   Date

2 Deck Work

CAN:

* Prepare an anchor, mooring warps and take charge on deck when mooring alongside, coming to a buoy, anchoring, weighing anchor and slipping from a buoy or an alongside berth

* Additional for Sail:
  * Reef, shake out reefs and change sails to suit prevailing conditions

Instructor's signature *Sail*   *Motor*   Date

Recommended pre-course experience:			
Days at sea:	5	Night Hours:	4
Miles:	100	Days as Skipper:	0

Day Skipper

3 Navigation

Is proficient in chartwork and routine navigational duties on passage including:

KNOWLEDGE OF:

* The uses and limitations of AIS

UNDERSTANDS:

* Working up Dead Reckoning (DR) and Estimated Position (EP)
* Use of a lead line, or similar
* How to work out a course to steer to allow for set, drift and leeway

CAN:

* Take and plot visual fixes
* Use electronic navigation equipment for position fixing
* Use secondary means of position fixing
* Estimate tidal heights and tidal streams
* Use waypoints and routes
* Use knowledge of IALA buoyage
* Maintain navigational records
* Use an echo sounder

Instructor's signature *Sail*   *Motor*   Date

4 Pilotage

CAN:

* Prepare and execute a pilotage plan for entry into, or departure from, harbour
* Use leading and clearing lines
* Use transits and soundings as aids to pilotage

Instructor's signature *Sail*   *Motor*   Date

5 Meteorology

UNDERSTANDS:

* How to interpret shipping forecasts and use a barometer as a forecasting aid

CAN:

* Source forecast information

Instructor's signature *Sail*   *Motor*   Date

6 Rules of the Road

CAN:

* Demonstrate suitable awareness of other water users both at sea and in close-quarter manoeuvring
* Demonstrate a practical understanding of the International Regulations for Preventing Collisions at Sea

Instructor's signature *Sail*   *Motor*   Date

7 Maintenance and Repair Work

KNOWLEDGE OF:

* The properties and uses of common synthetic-fibre ropes

UNDERSTANDS:

* Maintenance tasks and is able to carry them out

Instructor's signature *Sail*   *Motor*   Date

8 Engines

Has a working knowledge of the prevention of common engine faults and is competent in the following areas:

UNDERSTANDS:

* The need for periodic maintenance checks on engines and electrical installations
* Requirements for tool kits, spares and lubricants
* The location of filters and bleed points for fuel
* The tension of drive belts and how to adjust or replace them

CAN:

* Carry out checks before starting, while running and after stopping
* Clean water filters and knows the location of impellors
* Estimate fuel consumption at various speeds and knows the effects of fouling
* Carry out basic troubleshooting

Instructor's signature *Sail*   *Motor*   Date

9 Victualling

UNDERSTANDS:

* How to victual a cruising vessel appropriately for the planned passage

Instructor's signature *Sail*   *Motor*   Date

10 Emergency Situations

UNDERSTANDS:

- How to issue distress signals by all available means, including distress flares and a VHF radio, in an emergency
- How to use a life raft
- How to secure a tow
- Rescue procedures including helicopter rescue
- The effects of cold-water shock on a casualty in the water
- The aftercare requirements of a casualty who has been in the water

CAN:

- Carry out the correct action as skipper for the recovery of a man overboard

Instructor's signature *Sail* _____ *Motor* _____ Date _____

11 Handling under Power (Sail and Motor)

KNOWLEDGE OF:

- Effects of waves on boat handling and crew comfort

UNDERSTANDS:

- Differing styles of hull and propulsion systems
- How to moor and leave a bow/stern-to mooring (practical experience where possible)
- How to identify and take into account wind and current conditions when planning and executing manoeuvres (practical experience where possible)

CAN:

- Carry out the following manoeuvres under power:
  - Steer a straight course
  - Turn in a confined space
  - Anchor at a pre-determined position
  - Berth alongside
  - Leave an alongside berth
  - Pick up a mooring buoy
- Additional for Motor vessels:
  - Use power and trim tabs correctly

Instructor's signature *Sail* _____ *Motor* _____ Date _____

12 Yacht Handling under Sail (Sail Only)

UNDERSTANDS:

- The characteristics of different types of keel
- How to identify and take into account wind and current conditions when planning and executing manoeuvres and choosing appropriate sail plan (practical experience where possible)

CAN:

- Bring a boat safely to and from a mooring buoy
- Anchor
- Steer and trim sails effectively on all points of sailing

Instructor's signature *Sail* _____ Date _____

13 Passage-making

KNOWLEDGE OF:

- Marina locks

UNDERSTANDS:

- The practical benefits and limitations of a chart plotter or GNSS

CAN:

- Plan and make a coastal passage, taking into account relevant navigational hazards and limitations imposed by the type of boat and the strength of the crew

Instructor's signature *Sail* _____ *Motor* _____ Date _____

14 Night Cruising

KNOWLEDGE OF:

- Has experienced cruising at night, including leaving and entering harbour

UNDERSTANDS:

- Special considerations for pilotage plans, keeping a lookout and identifying marks by night

Instructor's signature *Sail* _____ *Motor* _____ Date _____

Next Steps

You now need to consolidate your training and gain skippering experience in waters with which you are familiar. When planning for going further afield and boating in an area with which you are unfamiliar, you should research whether the area is affected by any characteristics that you did not experience on your course, such as katabatic winds, a different buoyage system (IALA A/B or CEVNI), large tidal streams or range, or different berthing arrangements (e.g. Med moorings). If your research shows further training would be prudent, please contact an RYA centre in that area.

Advanced Pilotage

The Advanced Pilotage course aims to build on the skills attained by the sailor at Day Skipper level. You will gain confidence in your pilotage skills and in navigating at night. A sailor undertaking this course might not yet have the experience required for Coastal Skipper.

Recommended prior learning: VHF/SRC (Short Range Certificate); first aid; knowledge to the level of RYA Coastal Skipper/Yachtmaster Theory.

Duration: Two days.

Minimum age: 17.

Non-residential course.

1 Passage Planning

UNDERSTANDS:

- Victualling
- The importance of identifying ports of refuge
- The publications required
- Strategy
- Customs procedures

CAN:

- Calculate the fuel required, including reserve
- Plan a coastal passage

Instructor's signature _____   Date _____

2 Preparation for Sea

UNDERSTANDS:

- Safety equipment for offshore passages

CAN:

- Prepare a motor cruiser for sea
- Give an effective safety briefing

Instructor's signature _____   Date _____

Recommended pre-course experience:			
Days at sea:	10	Night Hours:	4
Miles:	150	Days as Skipper:	2

3 Pilotage

UNDERSTANDS:

- Tidal considerations
- GNSS limitations in pilotage

CAN:

- Prepare a pilotage plan taking into consideration soundings, transits, clearing bearings, back bearings, buoyage, and port or harbour regulations
- Pilot a motor cruiser by day and night

Instructor's signature   Date

4 Passage-making and Responsibility as a Skipper (Daylight Hours)

UNDERSTANDS:

- The significance of meteorological trends
- The importance of crew welfare, safety and control on passage

CAN:

- Take charge of a motor cruiser and direct the crew
- Organise the navigational, deck work, and domestic duties for a motor cruiser on passage
- Organise watch-keeping
- Integrate the use of traditional and electronic aids to navigation

Instructor's signature   Date

5 Radar/AIS

KNOWLEDGE OF:

- The uses and limitations of AIS

UNDERSTANDS:

- The advantages and limitations of radar

Instructor's signature   Date

6 Boat Handling

UNDERSTANDS:

* The characteristics of various hull forms and propeller configurations

CAN:

* Control the boat effectively in a confined space, including all berthing and unberthing situations in various conditions of wind and tide
* Berth and unberth in simple situations using one engine and lines (on a twin-engine boat)
* Avoid excessive use of power
* Demonstrate a practical understanding and correct use of power trim and trim tabs

Instructor's signature _____ Date _____

7 Adverse Weather Conditions

UNDERSTANDS:

* The action to be taken in rough weather
* The importance of boat control in waves, and positioning to minimise the possibility of injury
* Preparation for heavy weather and handling in strong winds
* Navigation and general conduct in restricted visibility

Instructor's signature _____ Date _____

8 Emergency Situations

KNOWLEDGE OF:

* How a vessel may be asked to assist in a search

UNDERSTANDS:

* The actions to be taken when abandoning to a life raft, and during helicopter and lifeboat rescues
* What to do in a medical emergency
* Towing and being towed
* How to issue distress signals by all available means in an emergency, including distress flares and a VHF radio

CAN:

* Recover a man-overboard dummy by day and night in all available conditions

Instructor's signature _____ Date _____

9 Night Cruising

CAN:

* Take charge of a motor cruiser at night, including entering and leaving harbour
* Demonstrate the ability to keep a proper lookout and identify lit marks and nominated positions by night

Instructor's signature _____ Date _____

Coastal Skipper

The aim of the course is to teach the skills and techniques required to skipper a cruising yacht (for the Sail course) or motor cruiser (for the Motor course), of 7 metres LWL to 15 metres LOA, safely on coastal and offshore passages by day and night. Students will gain practice in planning and skippering longer passages with a significant number of night hours where watch-keeping rotas become relevant. At the end of the course a successful candidate would be awarded a course completion certificate.

The minimum age for the award of the certificate is 17.

1 Passage Planning

KNOWLEDGE OF:

- The effects of fouling on boat speed and fuel consumption

UNDERSTANDS:

- Fuel consumption at different speeds and can calculate fuel required for a passage, including reserve
- Customs procedures
- Stability

CAN:

- Plan a coastal passage, taking into consideration the capability of the vessel, navigation, victualling, weather, ports of refuge, tidal heights and tidal streams, publications required, and strategy

Instructor's signature *Sail* _____ *Motor* _____ Date _____

2 Preparation for Sea

UNDERSTANDS:

- What safety equipment is required for offshore passages

CAN:

- Prepare a cruising vessel for sea, including stowage, safety briefing, watchkeeping, delegating responsibilities, equipment, and engine checks

Instructor's signature *Sail* _____ *Motor* _____ Date _____

3 Pilotage

CAN:

- Prepare a pilotage plan, taking into consideration soundings, transits, clearing bearings, buoyage, port or harbour regulations, and tidal factors
- Pilot a cruising vessel by day and at night

Instructor's signature *Sail* _____ *Motor* _____ Date _____

Recommended pre-course experience:			
Days at sea:	15	Night Hours:	8
Miles:	300	Days as Skipper:	2

4 Passage-making and Ability as Skipper

UNDERSTANDS:

- The practical uses of integrated electronic aids to navigation, including AIS, radar, electronic navigational charts (ENCs), and raster navigational charts (RNCs)

CAN:

- Take charge of a yacht and direct the crew
- Organise the navigation, deck work and domestic duties of a cruising vessel on passage
- Be aware of the significance of meteorological trends
- Be aware of crew welfare on passage
- Use electronic navigational equipment for planning and undertaking a passage, including the use of waypoints and routes

Instructor's signature *Sail* _____ *Motor* _____ _____ Date _____

5 Yacht Handling under Power

UNDERSTANDS:

- How to identify and take into account wind and current conditions when planning and executing manoeuvres (practical experience where possible)

CAN:

- Control the cruising vessel effectively in a confined space under power, including all berthing and unberthing situations
- Pick up a mooring bow- or stern-to
- Avoid excessive use of power
- Additional for twin-engined vessels:
  - Berth and unberth in simple situations using one engine, including the correct use of lines

Instructor's signature *Sail* _____ *Motor* _____ Date _____

6 Yacht Handling under Sail

UNDERSTANDS:

- How to identify and take into account wind and current conditions when planning and executing manoeuvres (practical experience where possible)

CAN:

- Use the sails to control the yacht in a confined space
- Consistently pick up a mooring
- Sail efficiently on all points of sail, including downwind techniques

Instructor's signature *Sail* _____ Date _____

7 Adverse Weather Conditions

UNDERSTANDS:

- How to handle a cruising vessel in strong winds
- General conduct in restricted visibility

CAN:

- Prepare a cruising vessel for heavy weather
- Navigate in restricted visibility

Instructor's signature *Sail*   *Motor*   Date

8 Emergency Situations

UNDERSTANDS:

- The actions to be taken when abandoning to a life raft, and during helicopter and lifeboat rescues
- How to carry out the aftercare requirements on a casualty who has been in the water

CAN:

- Describe to a crew member the effects of cold-water shock on a casualty who has been in the water
- Recover a man overboard under power
- Additional for Sail:
  - Recover a man overboard under sail

Instructor's signature *Sail*   *Motor*   Date

Next Steps

The Coastal Skipper course is the highest certified course within the RYA Yachtmaster Scheme, but this does not signal the end of your development. You now need to consolidate your training and gain experience with longer passages in a range of conditions. When planning for going further afield and boating in an area with which you are unfamiliar, you should research whether the area is affected by any characteristics that you have not experienced, such as katabatic winds, different buoyage systems (IALA A/B or CEVNI), large tidal streams or range, or different berthing arrangements (e.g. Med moorings). Most RYA training centres offer bespoke training to address any specific areas of interest.

RYA Yachtmaster Exam Preparation

Most RYA centres offering the RYA Yachtmaster Scheme offer some form of pre-exam preparation or coaching for those looking to take an RYA Yachtmaster exam at Coastal or Offshore level. These courses are often referred to as an 'RYA Yachtmaster prep' course/week. This is unique within the RYA training framework in that it does not have a fixed course syllabus, length or course completion certificate. However, RYA Yachtmaster preparation training is generally five days long and followed by the practical exam.

What is Expected of you Prior to the Training?

To attend RYA Yachtmaster preparation training, the school and the Instructor will expect that you have all the prerequisites to be eligible for an RYA Yachtmaster Coastal or RYA Yachtmaster Offshore exam (page 70). In addition, they will be expecting a suitably experienced skipper and yachtsman/woman who can competently handle a boat under sail/power in close-quarter situations and at sea, and has a depth of knowledge equivalent to that gained from attending an RYA Yachtmaster Shorebased course. Perhaps most importantly, this knowledge should have been applied in a variety of situations during day and night passages. For those that have not attended and passed an RYA Yachtmaster Theory course, it is strongly recommended that you do so prior to attending RYA Yachtmaster preparation training.

What should you Expect from the Training?

Many schools run it as a stand-alone five-day course, although there could be students from any RYA practical courses up to the Day Skipper level with you on the yacht. Generally there should not be more than four RYA Yachtmaster candidates on a prep course due to the relatively intensive nature of the training and the need to ensure adequate contact time for each candidate.

The course content will depend upon the needs of all candidates and it is important to note that the course is aimed at fine-tuning existing skills rather than teaching new ones. During the course you will spend a lot of time cruising at night, and carry out various challenging boat-handing exercises under power/sail while employing all your existing RYA Yachtmaster Theory knowledge. The syllabus that the Instructor will use to shape your course will be the exam syllabus on pages 74–76. Read through the exam syllabus and be brutally honest with yourself about what you do/don't know, can/cannot do or have little experience of. Try to address any shortfalls prior to the course, and then be honest about your ability with your Instructor from the start. This will help the Instructor create the correct training package for the group and each individual.

Am I Ready for the Exam?

During the training the Instructor should frequently update you on your levels of ability (if not, please ask them). They will also guide you at the end on what exam you should aim at (RYA Yachtmaster Coastal or RYA Yachtmaster Offshore), or indeed what further training you should do prior to attempting an exam. An RYA Yachtmaster Instructor is highly experienced, so please listen to the advice given; they have first-hand experience of the RYA Yachtmaster exam, and have undertaken significant additional training and assessment to get to the level of RYA Yachtmaster Instructor.

As a guide, if you are learning something for the first time on an RYA Yachtmaster prep course, or your Instructor is suggesting you are not at the required standard, you should think carefully about whether you are ready for the exam.

Personal Log

For the personal log to be of value it must be filled in accurately and comprehensively. The columns have particular significance in relation to the experience required before examination for Certificates of Competence.

Personal Log – Cruises and/or Races

The following notes give guidance on the information to be included and define the terms used.

Column 2 – Name of Vessel

The vessel must be over 7 metres LWL. If using mileage on a vessel over 24 metres LOA, please ensure you record the tonnage.

Column 3 – Details of Voyage

It is most important that this includes a record of the capacity in which the cruise was made (e.g. crew member, mate of watch, skipper etc.).

Column 4 – Days on Board

A day on board is a period of eight consecutive hours living on board the vessel, the majority of which the vessel should have been at sea. Periods of fewer than eight hours may not be aggregated to increase the total but a day is not invalidated by leaving the yacht for a few hours during a cruise. Only one eight-hour period may be counted in any 24 consecutive hours, i.e. 16 hours on board would count as one day on board.[1]

Column 5 – Distance Logged

This is the distance sailed by the log, in the open sea, outside natural or artificial harbours, in which it would be possible to leave a yacht secured or anchored unattended for a prolonged period.

Tidal or Non-tidal? An area is deemed tidal if published stream, current or tidal-range data is available, the influence of which is significant enough to require the effects to be taken into account to plan and execute a safe and efficient passage.

Column 6 – Night Hours

These are hours on watch or taking an active part in the navigation or handling of the yacht, at sea between sunset and sunrise.

Column 7 – Signature of Skipper

Holders of logbooks may sign for cruises during which they were the skipper of the yacht.

---

[1] The MCA defines seatime in great detail. Refer to the MCA website

Retrospective Logging of Experience

Page 47 includes a section for you to record, in general terms, experience gained prior to acquiring this logbook. The prerequisite seatime for examinations for RYA Yachtmaster Offshore and RYA Yachtmaster Coastal must have been gained within the 10 years preceding the examination. The section provides space for a summary of your experience obtained prior to keeping formal records, while the subsequent pages provide a useful way for you to log seatime in the future.

Logging Commercial Hours

If you spend days on board which are shorter than eight hours, for example work shift patterns, please contact the RYA for advice on how to log those hours. Those with aspirations to move towards higher-level commercial qualifications should consider obtaining a Seaman's Discharge book or other similar document issued by the regulatory body for the country whose qualifications they hold. This will allow seatime to be logged in a format that can be officially verified.

Summary of Experience Prior to Record in Personal Log

Year	Broad Details of Experience [1]	Estimated			Skipper's Signature [2]
		Days on Board	Distance Logged	Night Hours	

[1] Include boats sailed, sailing area and capacity in which sailed
[2] If available

Personal Log of Cruises and/or Races

1. Dates From–To	2. Name of Vessel Class; size inc. length or tonnage; sail or motor	3. Details of Voyage Max. wind force; ports visited; capacity in which sailing	4. Days on Board	5. Distance Logged Tidal/Non-Tidal	6. Night Hours	7. Skipper's Signature
Specimen entry 19–27 July 2014	Wave Glider; Farr 38 sailing yacht	Namley Harbour – Port Fraser – Rozelle Cove – Dawson Harbour – Namley Harbour	6	150 Tidal	6	Graham Hwans

Totals carried forward

49

Personal Log of Cruises and/or Races

1. Dates From–To	2. Name of Vessel Class; size inc. length or tonnage; sail or motor	3. Details of Voyage Max. wind force; ports visited; capacity in which sailing	4. Days on Board	5. Distance Logged Tidal/Non-Tidal	6. Night Hours	7. Skipper's Signature

Personal Log of Cruises and/or Races

1. Dates From-To	2. Name of Vessel Class; size inc. length or tonnage; sail or motor	3. Details of Voyage Max. wind force; ports visited; capacity in which sailing	4. Days on Board	5. Distance Logged Tidal/Non-Tidal	6. Night Hours	7. Skipper's Signature

51

Personal Log of Cruises and/or Races

1. Dates From–To	2. Name of Vessel Class; size inc. length or tonnage; sail or motor	3. Details of Voyage Max. wind force; ports visited; capacity in which sailing	4. Days on Board	5. Distance Logged Tidal/Non-Tidal	6. Night Hours	7. Skipper's Signature

Totals brought forward

Totals carried forward

52

Personal Log of Cruises and/or Races

Totals brought forward

1. Dates From–To	2. Name of Vessel Class; size inc. length or tonnage; sail or motor	3. Details of Voyage Max. wind force; ports visited; capacity in which sailing	4. Days on Board	5. Distance Logged Tidal/Non-Tidal	6. Night Hours	7. Skipper's Signature

Totals carried forward

53

Personal Log of Cruises and/or Races

Totals brought forward

Totals carried forward

1. Dates From–To	2. Name of Vessel Class; size inc. length or tonnage; sail or motor	3. Details of Voyage Max. wind force; ports visited; capacity in which sailing	4. Days on Board	5. Distance Logged Tidal/Non-Tidal	6. Night Hours	7. Skipper's Signature

54

Personal Log of Cruises and/or Races

Totals brought forward

Totals carried forward

1. Dates From–To	2. Name of Vessel Class; size inc. length or tonnage; sail or motor	3. Details of Voyage Max. wind force; ports visited; capacity in which sailing	4. Days on Board	5. Distance Logged Tidal/Non-Tidal	6. Night Hours	7. Skipper's Signature

55

Personal Log of Cruises and/or Races

Totals brought forward

1. Dates From–To	2. Name of Vessel Class; size inc. length or tonnage; sail or motor	3. Details of Voyage Max. wind force; ports visited; capacity in which sailing	4. Days on Board	5. Distance Logged Tidal/Non-Tidal	6. Night Hours	7. Skipper's Signature

Totals carried forward

Personal Log of Cruises and/or Races

Totals brought forward

1. Dates From–To	2. Name of Vessel Class; size inc. length or tonnage; sail or motor	3. Details of Voyage Max. wind force; ports visited; capacity in which sailing	4. Days on Board	5. Distance Logged Tidal/Non-Tidal	6. Night Hours	7. Skipper's Signature

Totals carried forward

Personal Log of Cruises and/or Races

1. Dates From-To	2. Name of Vessel Class; size inc. length or tonnage; sail or motor	3. Details of Voyage Max. wind force; ports visited; capacity in which sailing	4. Days on Board	5. Distance Logged Tidal/Non-Tidal	6. Night Hours	7. Skipper's Signature

Totals brought forward

Totals carried forward

Personal Log of Cruises and/or Races

1. Dates From-To	2. Name of Vessel Class; size inc. length or tonnage; sail or motor	3. Details of Voyage Max. wind force; ports visited; capacity in which sailing	4. Days on Board	5. Distance Logged Tidal/Non-Tidal	6. Night Hours	7. Skipper's Signature

Summary of Personal Log

	Days	Distance Logged	Night Hours
Totals for 20			
Totals for 20			
Totals for 20			
Totals for 20			
Totals for 20			
Totals for 20			
Totals for 20			
Totals for 20			
Totals for 20			
Totals for 20			
Totals			

RYA/MCA Examinations and Certificates of Competence

Many yachtsmen and women would agree that the RYA Yachtmaster Coastal and RYA Yachtmaster Offshore examinations are the most useful and credible of all yachting qualifications. The RYA administers the RYA Yachtmaster Scheme and examines candidates on behalf of the UK Maritime and Coastguard Agency. The qualification is accepted as a worldwide standard. The examination is a one-day examination of the candidate's ability to skipper a yacht.

Examinations for RYA/MCA Certificates of Competence

RYA/MCA Yachtmaster Coastal, RYA Yachtmaster Offshore and RYA Yachtmaster Ocean Certificates of Competence are gained by examinations that are conducted by RYA Yachtmaster Examiners who are independent of RYA Training Centres. Details of the prerequisite experience and qualifications required before taking these examinations, and the scope of the syllabus, is shown on the following pages. There is no formal requirement to attend a training course before taking an examination, although candidates who have no formal maritime training will be unlikely to succeed in the exam without a substantial amount of study and preparation. RYA Yachtmaster examination candidates should ensure that they are familiar with the handling and other characteristics of any vessel they intend to use for their examination.

Vessels used for Sport or Recreation on a Commercial Basis

Vessels used for sport or recreation on a commercial basis are subject to Merchant Shipping legislation published in MGN 280. The use of RYA Yachtmaster Coastal, Offshore and Ocean certificates is permitted for the skippers of these vessels, provided that the certificates are commercially endorsed.

To obtain this endorsement an applicant must obtain a Medical Fitness Certificate, a Professional Practices and Responsibilities Certificate, an RYA or equivalent first aid certificate, and attend a Basic Sea Survival Course.

Medical fitness forms and details of the relevant specialist courses are available from the RYA at www.rya.org.uk. The endorsement for commercial use can be valid for up to five years. It may be renewed by providing evidence of continuing satisfactory service at sea as skipper or mate of a small commercial vessel and a Medical Fitness Certificate.

In addition, all commercially endorsed RYA Yachtmaster Offshore and RYA Yachtmaster Ocean certificates include the following wording:

This certificate is valid for use as Master of Yachts up to 200gt on commercially and privately registered yachts until (date of expiry).

Superyacht Qualifications

UK commercial pleasure vessels of more than 24 metres load line length are subject to the Training and Certification Guidance MSN 1858.

Full details of MSN 1858 and MGN 280 are given on the Maritime and Coastguard Agency website www.mcga.gov.uk.

RYA/MCA Certificates of Competence with a commercial endorsement can be used for watchkeeping and command positions on a variety of different-sized vessels and as an entry into MCA qualifications.

STCW-endorsed RYA Yachtmaster Certificates

Under British Maritime and Coastguard Agency (MCA) regulations, skippers holding an RYA Yachtmaster Offshore or RYA Yachtmaster Ocean Certificate of Competence with a commercial endorsement may be the master of yachts and pleasure vessels up to 200gt.

However, some professional sectors, particularly those that operate extensively in non-UK-coastal states, may require seafarers to have attended four courses that comply with the international STCW '78 (as amended) convention.

These courses are:

- STCW Personal Survival Techniques: STCW A-V1/1-1, or RYA Sea Survival
- STCW Personal Safety and Social Responsibilities: STCW A-V1/1-4
- STCW Elementary First Aid: STCW A-V1/1-3
- STCW Firefighting and Fire Prevention: STCW A–V1/1-2

Holders of the RYA Yachtmaster Offshore or Ocean Certificates of Competence who have successfully completed these courses may have their RYA certificate of competence endorsed with the following words to verify completion of these courses:

The certificate holder has completed training under the STCW code A-V1/1 Para 2.1. This certificate is valid for use as Master of Yachts of up to 200gt on commercially and privately registered yachts until (date of expiry).

If you require this endorsement you may obtain a new certificate by applying to the RYA with:

- A covering letter requesting the STCW endorsement
- Your original certificate
- A new passport photograph
- Evidence of completion of the STCW courses
- A fee payable to the RYA

Withdrawal of Certificates

The RYA/MCA Yachtmaster Qualification Panel reserves the right to withdraw a certificate of competence at any time if due cause is shown.

Own-boat Exams

For the Practical examination for RYA Yachtmaster Coastal and RYA Yachtmaster Offshore, candidates must provide a sail/motor cruising vessel (as appropriate), not less than 7 metres (LWL) and no more than 18 metres (LOA), in sound, seaworthy condition and equipped to the standard set out in G103 *RYA Boat Safety Handbook*. The yacht must be equipped with a full and up-to-date set of charts and navigational publications and be efficiently crewed, as the Examiner will not take part in the management of the yacht during the examination. The vessel must be appropriate for the purpose of an RYA/MCA Yachtmaster examination and the RYA reserves the right to refuse examination in the event that the vessel is not suitable for that purpose.

Booking an Examination (within the UK)

You can book an exam via the RYA website www.rya.org.uk.

Serving British military personnel should contact their relevant sailing association for details of examination arrangements.

Exams through an RYA Training Centre

If you take a Practical course at an RYA Training Centre the exam can be arranged through the centre.

Exams outside the UK

Overseas examinations must be organised through an RYA Training Centre recognised for Practical cruising courses for the discipline in which the exam is being taken. The overseas exam location must be approved by the RYA.

Exams in New Zealand are organised through CBES: RYAinfo@cbes.org.nz.

Exams in Australia may be organised through Yachting Australia: training@yachting.org.au.

RYA/MCA Yachtmaster Examinations

Record of Qualifying Passages

Full details of the qualifying passages required for the RYA Yachtmaster Offshore examination should be recorded on page 77.

Quality of Experience

The requirements for experience prior to examination for RYA/MCA certificates can only be defined in quantitative terms.

However, the quality of experience is just as important and, although it would be impossible to lay down absolute requirements without producing an unduly complicated and restrictive set of rules, the attention of all candidates is drawn to the following notes.

Examiners are responsible for establishing the level of a candidate's competence during the exam. Where a candidate's qualifying mileage is doubtful, Examiners will question the candidate carefully.

Geographical Breadth of Experience

It is relatively simple to visit harbours and anchorages with which one is familiar and has local knowledge. However, a competent yachtsman should be able to enter any harbour in which there is sufficient depth, given an adequate chart and sailing directions.

The skill of interpreting published information on unfamiliar harbours is best acquired by practice, and every opportunity should be taken to visit small harbours and anchorages.

Entering harbour by night calls for an acquired skill in identifying navigational lights or picking out unlit marks against the background of the shore lights. Again, practice is the key to success.

It is essential that candidates satisfy all prerequisite mileage, experience and courses prior to applying to undertake the exam. Candidates with little or no experience of being in charge of a vessel will have little hope of success and will do themselves no favours by putting themselves forward for the exam. The prerequisite experience has been carefully determined to ensure that candidates are likely to have had adequate opportunity to properly develop the skills and knowledge on which they will be examined.

Equally, it is important to note that mileage being claimed for the purpose of exam prerequisites should be accrued on appropriate vessels. For example, a candidate who has accrued all of their seatime on a vessel over, say, 45 metres will have had no opportunity to 'command' the vessel and is unlikely to have accrued any significant boat-handling experience. For this reason **at least 50 per cent of the minimum seatime for RYA Yachtmaster exam candidates must have been accrued on vessels less than 24 metres LOA**. Vessels on which seatime has been accrued must be relevant to the type of exam which is to be undertaken.

Virtually anything within the RYA Yachtmaster Scheme (with the exception of the material relating to RYA Yachtmaster Ocean) falls within the scope of the RYA Yachtmaster Practical examination. However, the points below are intended to provide prospective candidates with an understanding of the areas for focus.

Navigation

You must know your position reasonably accurately throughout the exam, but don't make the mistake of being so busy plotting fixes that you forget to look around you. Often, a quick glance on deck will confirm your position from a buoy or transit.

Make sure you know how to use any electronic aids to navigation on board, particularly a GNSS/chart plotter, but there is no need to over-navigate.

You will usually be given practical problems involving tidal streams and heights. Make life easy for yourself and look them up beforehand – it's not cheating. Practise a few tidal calculations so you are happy with the methods you are going to use.

Boat Handling

You need to know how your boat will react, its turning circle and any predictable quirks to its handling. There will be some close-quarters manoeuvring, usually in a harbour, to demonstrate your skills at berthing and leaving pontoons, piles or moorings. Sailing yachts will complete this section under power, but make sure you practise manoeuvring under sail too, such as picking up mooring buoys and short tacking. Candidates for RYA Yachtmaster Sail exams will also be asked to demonstrate their close-quarter sailing skills.

Your Examiner isn't looking for first-time-every-time success, but you will need to demonstrate competence and a good understanding of how the boat reacts at slow speed. Don't hesitate to change sails or reef if you think it is necessary for the task.

Experience in a variety of conditions will be your biggest help in these situations.

Man Overboard

Exams almost always include a man-overboard recovery exercise. The multitude of methods for this can be confusing, but pick one that works for you and your boat. However it's done, you must end up with the yacht stopped next to the man in the water. If you're sailing, the Examiner will clarify if he/she wants you to carry out the exercise under power or sail. If in doubt, use the engine.

Safety

Make sure you understand and follow safety procedures, and give a safety brief. If you decide that safety tethers should be worn at night, take your own advice. As the exam candidate you are responsible for the safety of the crew and the boat, and the Examiner is looking to determine whether you fully appreciate and are capable of that responsibility.

Meteorology

Obtain a forecast before your exam and be prepared for questions about the current weather and how this might affect a passage plan. Understand how weather systems influence sea conditions and how to plan based on this knowledge. The type of boat and the strengths of your crew can have a bearing on decisions based on the weather, so your Examiner may ask you to consider various possibilities. There is rarely a definitive answer, so it is your informed opinions that are required.

Adverse Weather Conditions

Skippers are most thoroughly tested when they have to cope with gale-force winds or fog at sea. It is possible, by sailing within strict self-imposed limits and never making passages which place the yacht more than a few hours from a safe harbour, to avoid adverse weather conditions, but to do so invariably limits experience. It is not recommended that anyone should go to sea under adverse conditions for the sole purpose of experiencing a gale or fog, but neither should candidates for RYA/MCA certificates adopt an over-cautious approach.

Skippering Ability

This is where your experience and knowledge will really show. Whether you are fully in command of the yacht is the most important assessment that your Examiner will make.

A good skipper leads the crew and communicates with them, making sure they understand what is going on and listening to them when they have something to say. They do not shout a stream of commands, leaving their crew in a quivering mess. Quiet competence instils confidence, helping your crew feel safe in the knowledge that the right decisions are being made. The command and communication skills of the candidate will form a key part of the exam process.

Long Passages

In many parts of the world, particularly in popular yachting centres, it is possible to cruise over a wide area without ever making a passage longer than 18–24 hours. Such passages can be accomplished without the need for an effective watchkeeping system and tend to encourage day sailing rather than passage-making. Candidates should endeavour to gain experience of longer passages of two or three days or more to ensure that they understand how a yacht and crew should be managed during a prolonged period at sea.

RYA Yachtmaster Coastal Certificate of Competence

The RYA Yachtmaster Coastal has the knowledge needed to skipper a sailing yacht/ motor cruiser on coastal cruises but does not necessarily have the experience needed to undertake longer passages.

Exam Duration

The exam will take about six to 10 hours for one candidate and/or four to eight hours per candidate where more than one candidate is being examined. No more than two candidates may be examined in any 24-hour period and no more than four candidates may be on the vessel at any given time.

Candidates will be set tasks to allow them to demonstrate their ability and will also be asked questions on any part of the syllabus for all Practical and Shorebased courses up to Coastal Skipper level.

Pre-exam Requirements

To take the Practical examination, candidates must be aged 17 or over and require:

* A Radio Operator's Qualification – A GMDSS Short Range Certificate (SRC) or higher grade of marine radio certificate

* A valid first aid certificate. Visit www.rya.org.uk for more information about suitable first aid certificates.

* Seatime – 800 miles logged within 10 years prior to examination, 30 days living on board, two days as skipper and 12 night hours

For holders of the Coastal Skipper Practical Course Completion Certificate, the seatime requirement is reduced to 400 miles, 20 days living on board, 12 night hours, two days as skipper.

Half of the qualifying seatime must have been gained in tidal waters. For sizes of vessel, please see the tables on page 73.

Visit www.rya.org.uk for further information on the definition of a qualifying passage.

RYA Yachtmaster Offshore Certificate of Competence

The RYA Yachtmaster Offshore is competent to skipper a sailing yacht/motor cruiser on any passage during which the vessel is no more than 150 miles from harbour.

Exam Duration

The exam will take about eight to 12 hours for one candidate and between five and nine hours per candidate where more than one candidate is being examined. No more than two candidates may be examined in any 24-hour period.

Candidates will be set tasks to allow them to demonstrate their ability as skipper of an offshore cruising yacht/motor cruiser and may also be asked questions on any part of the syllabus for all courses except RYA Yachtmaster Ocean.

Pre-exam Requirements

To be eligible to take the Practical examination, candidates must be aged 18 or over and require:

- A Radio Operator's Qualification – A GMDSS Short Range Certificate (SRC) or higher grade of marine radio certificate
- A valid first aid certificate. Visit www.rya.org.uk for more information about suitable first aid certificates.
- Seatime – 50 days, 2,500 miles within 10 years prior to the examination, including at least five passages over 60 miles, acting as skipper for at least two of these passages and including two which have involved overnight passages. Five days' experience as skipper. At least half the qualifying seatime must have been accrued in tidal waters. For sizes of vessel please see the tables on page 73.

Qualifying passages for RYA Yachtmaster Ocean and Offshore must be non-stop, by the shortest navigable route with no change of skipper. Passages such as recognised races which may not comply exactly with these requirements may be submitted to the RYA for approval before the voyage.

Trainee skippers undertaking 60-mile passages are strongly advised to take a Coastal Skipper course first.

Visit www.rya.org.uk for further information on the definition of a qualifying passage.

Conversion Practical Examinations

Holders of the RYA Yachtmaster Coastal or RYA Yachtmaster Offshore Sail Certificate may take a conversion examination to obtain the RYA Yachtmaster Coastal or RYA Yachtmaster Offshore Power Certificate.

Candidates may also convert to sail. The same rules apply but the conversion exam will be slightly longer.

The exam fee set by the RYA is less than a full examination on the basis that some material has previously been examined.

Exam Duration

The exam will take about three hours (longer for a motor to sail conversion). The Examiner may ask questions or set tasks on any part of the syllabus but will concentrate on those sections which are markedly different in a motor cruiser, e.g. boat handling, passage planning, radar.

Pre-exam Requirements

RYA Yachtmaster Coastal

At least half the required experience for RYA Yachtmaster Coastal must be in an appropriate vessel, i.e. a power vessel such as a motor cruiser, or a sail vessel such as a cruising yacht.

- Seatime: in all cases a minimum of 400 miles is required within 10 years prior to the examination
- 12 days living aboard
- Two days as skipper
- 12 night hours

For sizes of vessel, please see the tables on page 73.

RYA Yachtmaster Offshore

At least half the minimum required experience for RYA Yachtmaster Offshore must be in an appropriate vessel, i.e. a power vessel such as a motor cruiser or a sail vessel such as a cruising yacht.

- Minimum seatime: 1,250 miles within 10 years prior to the examination
- 25 days
- Three days as skipper
- Three passages over 60 miles, including one overnight and one as skipper

For sizes of vessel, please see the tables on page 73.

RYA Yachtmaster Ocean Certificate of Competence

The RYA Yachtmaster Ocean is experienced and competent to skipper a yacht on passages of any length in all parts of the world.

Form of Examination

The exam consists of an oral and a written test with the candidate having also already successfully completed a qualifying ocean passage.

Oral

The candidate must provide the Examiner with:

a) A narrative account of the planning and execution of the qualifying passage.

b) Navigational records, completed on board a yacht on passage, out of sight of land (or charted objects capable of being used for navigation/position fixing), showing that the candidate has navigated the yacht without the use of electronic navigational aids. The records must include as a minimum: planning, reduction and plotting of a sun-run-meridian altitude sight and a compass check carried out using the bearing of the sun, moon, a star or a planet.

During the oral test the candidate may be required to answer questions on all aspects of ocean passage-making in a yacht, including passage planning; navigation; worldwide meteorology; crew management and yacht preparation; maintenance, and repairs.

Written

The written exam will include questions on sights and sight reduction, and worldwide meteorology.

Candidates who hold the Certificate of Satisfactory Completion of the RYA/MCA Yachtmaster Ocean Shorebased Course[1], a Royal Navy Ocean Navigation Certificate, or an MCA Certificate of Competence as a Deck Officer will be exempt from the written examination.

[1] The exam must be invigilated for the candidate to be exempt from the written exam for the RYA Yachtmaster Ocean Certificate of Competence. This also applies to certificates used for entry into the superyacht qualification structure – see page 62.

Pre-exam Requirements

All candidates must:

(a) Hold an RYA/MCA Yachtmaster Offshore Certificate of Competence. An RYA/MCA Yachtmaster Coastal Certificate of Competence does not qualify.

(b) Have completed, as skipper or mate of a yacht, a qualifying passage which meets the following criteria:

> i) The candidate was fully involved with the planning of the passage within 10 years prior to the examination, including selection of the route; the navigational plan; checking the material condition of the yacht and her equipment; provisioning with spare gear; water and victuals, and organising the watch-keeping routine.

> ii) During the passage a minimum non-stop distance of 600 miles must have been run by the log, the yacht must have been at sea continuously for at least 96 hours, and the yacht must have been more than 50 miles from land or charted objects capable of being used for navigation/position fixing while sailing a distance of at least 200 miles.

> iii) For sizes of vessel, please see the tables on page 73.

(c) Hold a first aid qualification, as for RYA Yachtmaster Offshore.

For Ocean passages, the following definition will apply:

'Throughout the passage the candidate must have acted in a responsible capacity either in sole charge of a watch or as a skipper.'

Please note, performing the role of 'lookout' does not fulfil the eligibility requirements.

Ocean candidates may take their sights on a shorter passage than their qualifying passage. In this case the candidate must have left from one port while returning to a different port with astro navigation used to navigate along the rhumb line out of sight of land.

The Examiner will determine whether the candidate is competent at astro navigation.

Visit www.rya.org.uk for further information on the definition of a qualifying passage.

QUALIFYING PASSAGES		
Exam	Between 7m LWL and 24m LOA (less than 80gt)	Over 24m LOA up to 500gt
RYA YACHTMASTER COASTAL	YES	NO
RYA YACHTMASTER OFFSHORE	YES	NO
RYA YACHTMASTER OCEAN	YES	YES

QUALIFYING SEATIME			
Exam	Between 7m LWL and 24m LOA (less than 80gt)	Over 24 metres and Less than 200 gross tons	200 to 500 gross tons
RYA YACHTMASTER COASTAL	Yes[1]	Yes (Up to 50 per cent of the qualifying mileage and days)	Yes (Up to 50 per cent of the qualifying mileage and days)
RYA YACHTMASTER COASTAL CONVERSION	Yes[1]	Yes (Up to 50 per cent of the qualifying mileage and days)	Yes (Up to 50 per cent of the qualifying mileage and days)
RYA YACHTMASTER OFFSHORE	Yes[1]	Yes[2] (Up to 50 per cent of the qualifying mileage and days)	Yes[2] (Up to 50 per cent of the qualifying mileage and days)
RYA YACHTMASTER OFFSHORE CONVERSION	Yes[1]	Yes[2] (Up to 50 per cent of the qualifying mileage and days)	Yes[2] (Up to 50 per cent of the qualifying mileage and days)

The above guidance is not exhaustive and candidates may have significant seagoing experience on vessels not covered which may be considered. Contact the RYA Training Department for more information.

[1] At least 50 per cent of qualifying mileage must be completed on this size of vessel

[2] With supporting testimonials or a Seaman's Discharge book

RYA Yachtmaster Coastal and RYA Yachtmaster Offshore Exam Syllabus

Candidates will be given the opportunity to demonstrate knowledge and competence in many of the areas listed below. In each section the Examiner will expect to see the candidate take full responsibility for the management of the yacht and crew.

In RYA Yachtmaster Offshore exams the candidate will be expected to demonstrate competence based on broad experience.

In RYA Yachtmaster Coastal exams the candidate will be expected to demonstrate understanding but may not have had the opportunity to practise all aspects of the syllabus under a range of different weather conditions.

1 International Regulations for Preventing Collisions at Sea

Questions will be confined to the International Regulations and, although candidates must be aware of the existence of local regulations, they will not be expected to memorise specific local ones.

- General rules (1–3)
- Steering and sailing rules (4–19)
- Lights and shapes (20–31)
- Sound and light signals (32–37)
- Signals for vessels fishing in close proximity (Annex II)
- Distress signals (Annex IV)

2 Safety

Candidates will be expected to know what safety equipment should be carried on board a sailing yacht or motor vessel, based either on the recommendations in the *RYA Boat Safety Handbook* (G103), the World Sailing Special Regulations or the Codes of Practice for the Safety of Small Commercial Vessels. In particular, candidates must know the responsibilities of a skipper in relation to:

- The safety briefing
- Safety harnesses
- Life jackets
- Distress signalling (flares and electronic means)
- Stability
- Fire prevention and fighting
- Life rafts
- Knowledge of rescue procedures
- Helicopter rescue

3 Boat Handling

Candidates for RYA Yachtmaster Coastal examinations will be expected to answer questions or demonstrate ability in less-complex situations only. Candidates for RYA Yachtmaster Offshore will be expected to answer questions or demonstrate ability in more complex situations and will also be expected to show a higher level of expertise:

- Coming to and weighing anchor under power or sail in various conditions of wind and tide
- In all berthing and unberthing situations in various conditions of wind and tide
- In recovery of a man overboard and being able to describe the effects of cold-water shock and the aftercare requirements of a casualty who has been in the water
- When towing under open-sea conditions and in confined areas
- In boat handling in confined areas under sail
- In boat handling in heavy weather
- When using helmsmanship and sail trim to sail to best advantage
- Using warps for securing in an alongside berth and for shifting berth or winding

4 General seamanship, including maintenance

- Properties, use and care of synthetic-fibre ropes
- Knots
- General deck work at sea and in harbour
- Engine operations, routine checks and troubleshooting
- Improvisation of jury rigs following gear failure

5 Responsibilities of the Skipper

- Can skipper a yacht and manage the crew
- Communication with crew
- Delegation of responsibility and watchkeeping organisation
- Preparing the yacht for sea and for adverse weather
- Tactics for heavy weather and restricted visibility
- Emergency and distress situations
- Victualling for a cruise and feeding at sea
- Customs procedures
- Standards of behaviour and courtesy

6 Navigation

- Charts, navigational publications and sources of navigational information
- Chartwork, including position fixing and shaping course to allow for tidal stream and leeway
- Tidal height and stream calculations
- Buoyage and visual aids to navigation
- Instruments including compasses, logs, echo sounders, radio navigation aids, and chartwork instruments
- Passage planning and navigational tactics
- Pilotage techniques
- Navigational records
- The limits of navigational accuracy and margins of safety
- Lee shore dangers
- Use of electronic navigation aids for passage planning and navigation
- Use of waypoints and electronic routeing
- General understanding of AIS
- Navigational techniques for reduced visibility

7 Meteorology

- Definition of terms
- Sources of weather forecasts
- Weather systems and local weather effects
- Interpretation of weather forecasts, barometric trends and visible phenomena
- Ability to make passage-planning decisions based on forecast information

8 Signals

- Candidates for RYA Yachtmaster Coastal and Offshore must hold the SRC Certificate of Competence in radiotelephony or a higher grade of certificate in radiotelephony

RYA/MCA Yachtmaster Offshore Qualifying Passages

Port of Departure	Destination Time and Date	Vessel Details Power or Sail	Distance	Capacity on Board	Skipper's Signature
Specimen entry Namley Harbour 2000hrs 12/8/14	Port Southern 1345hrs 13/8/14	Sail	86 miles	Skipper	Sandra Lewcher

RYA/MCA Yachtmaster Ocean Passage

Passage completed on board yacht ....

Type of yacht, inc. LOA ....

Port of departure...Time/Date ....

Port of arrival ....Time/Date ....

Over 50M from land or charted
objects between position ....Time/Date ....

and position ....Time/Date ....

a total of .... hours, for a distance of .... miles

Sailing as skipper/mate of watch (delete as appropriate) throughout the passage.

Total distance sailed .... miles

Signature of Skipper ....

RYA Shorebased Courses

The Shorebased courses are designed to complement courses in the various RYA Practical schemes. The longer courses (40 hours) are typically run over five to six days of intensive tuition or spread over a number of weekends. Many schools offer different variations and others offer distance learning. Taking a one-day course will enable you to extend your knowledge and skills in a specialist area and some courses, such as the VHF Short Range Certificate, are a prerequisite for higher qualifications such as the RYA Yachtmaster Certificate of Competence.

Course Completion Certificates

The authority to award certificates of satisfactory completion of Shorebased courses is delegated to RYA Training Centres, which may be clubs, commercial sailing schools or distance-learning schools.

Certificates of satisfactory completion of courses are, as the name implies, awarded only following completion of a course. The Theory or written exams may not be taken as a separate process. However, anyone who has the necessary qualifying experience may take the full Practical examination for RYA Yachtmaster Coastal or RYA Yachtmaster Offshore Certificates of Competence (see page 68–70).

RYA Essential Navigation and Seamanship

There is no formal assessment on this 16-hour course. Candidates should have taken a full and active part in the course and performed adequately throughout.

Students should have an understanding of the principles taught during the course. This is an entry-level course and is ideal for those who are thinking about going boating or would like their first taste of RYA Shorebased training.

Day Skipper Shorebased Course

A standard set of assessment papers for this course is provided, along with numerous exercises. While many of these papers are used informally, some are worked under invigilation to provide an objective test of ability at the end of the course. The emphasis on this course is to demonstrate a sound understanding of the principles.

RYA Coastal Skipper/Yachtmaster Shorebased Course

This course also follows a set syllabus and has exercises and formal assessment papers contained in it. If the candidate intends to use the certificate from this course for the purpose of a higher-level MCA qualification prerequisite, they will need to ensure they undertake an invigilated exam. For this course, candidates are expected not only to understand principles but also to be able reach correct answers with the various assessment questions.

Layout of Syllabuses

An indication of the minimum recommended teaching time for each subject is given in each syllabus. The minimum time for the Day Skipper, and RYA Coastal Skipper and Yachtmaster Offshore syllabuses is 40 hours.

The courses also include exercise and assessment papers which involve an additional 14 hours' work.

Sufficient time should be allowed for completion of these exercises and subsequent discussion of them, together with additional exercises set by Instructors and revision. Actual course duration may therefore be as much as twice the minimum recommended teaching time. An indication of the depth of knowledge required is also given, with the following abbreviations being used:

A Full knowledge

B Working knowledge

C Outline knowledge

Within the Shorebased course framework there are different levels of knowledge required, depending upon the topic.

International Regulations for Preventing Collisions at Sea

Students are required to have a full knowledge of the regulations before completion of the Shorebased course for RYA Coastal Skipper and Yachtmaster Offshore. There is, however, insufficient time available in the course to teach the subject fully. The books G2 *RYA International Regulations for Preventing Collisions at Sea* or *A Seaman's Guide to the Rule of the Road* are useful books for study of the regulations. Study of this subject is strongly recommended prior to starting the course if you have no prior knowledge in this area.

Feedback

The student's assessment pack includes feedback forms about the courses. Please help the RYA to improve the courses by returning one to the school and the other to the RYA.

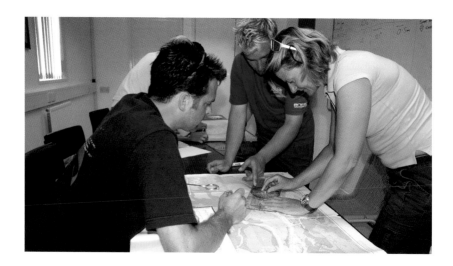

Essential Navigation and Seamanship Course Syllabus

The Essential Navigation and Seamanship course provides an introduction to the basic skills required before taking a small boat to sea or taking an active part in running a boat. The syllabus content is shown below.

	Minimum time (hours)
1 Charts, Publications and Terms	1

- Basic terms
- Chart overview
- Introduction to chart datum and depths

2 Buoyage	2

- Lateral buoys
- Cardinal buoys
- Where to find information

3 Navigation	1

- Plotting a position
- Measuring distance and bearing
- Position fix
- Heading

4 Safety	1

- Personal and boat-safety equipment
- Safety procedures and briefing
- Communications
- Engine checks
- Rescue procedures

5 Anchoring	1

- Where to anchor
- How to anchor

6 Tides	3

- Tidal streams
- Tidal heights

	Minimum time (hours)
7 Electronic Navigation	1
• GNSS terms	
• GNSS use	
• Using waypoints	
8 Rules of the Road	1
• Risk of collision	
• Who gives way	
9 Weather Forecasts	1
• Sources of forecast	
• Terms used in forecast	
10 Pilotage	1
• Harbour information	
• Transits	
• Pilotage plan	
11 Passage Planning	2
• SOLAS V requirements	
• Pre-planning	
• Chart choice	

Day Skipper Shorebased Course Syllabus

A comprehensive introduction to chartwork, navigation, meteorology and the basics of seamanship for Competent Crew. You will find this course invaluable if you want to learn how to start making decisions on board.

	Minimum time (hours)	Depth of knowledge
1 Nautical Terms	2	
• Parts of a boat and hull		B
• General nautical terminology		B
2 Ropework	0.5	
• Knowledge of the properties of synthetic ropes in common use		B
3 Anchorwork	1	
• Characteristics of different types of anchor		B
• Factors to take into account when anchoring		B
4 Safety	3	
• Knowledge of the safety equipment to be carried, its stowage and use (see G103 *RYA Boat Safety Handbook*)		B
• Fire precautions and firefighting		B
• Use of personal safety equipment, harnesses and life jackets		B
• Ability to send a distress signal by VHF radio		B
• Basic knowledge of rescue procedures including helicopter rescue		B
• Stability		C
5 International Regulations for Preventing Collisions at Sea	3	
• Steering and sailing rules (5, 7, 8, 9, 10 and 12–19)		A
• General rules (all other rules)		B
6 Definition of Position, Course and Speed	1	
• Latitude and longitude		B
• Knowledge of standard navigational terms		B
• True bearings and courses		B
• The knot		C

	Minimum time (hours)	Depth of knowledge
7 Navigational Charts and Publications	2	
• Information shown on charts, chart symbols and representation of direction and distance		B
• Navigational publications in common use		C
• Chart correction		C
8 Navigational Drawing Instruments	1	
• Use of parallel rulers, dividers and proprietary plotting instruments		B
9 Compass	2	
• Application of variation		B
• Awareness of deviation and its causes		C
• Use of hand-bearing compass		B
10 Chartwork and Navigation – Traditional and Electronic	6.5	
• Dead reckoning and estimated position		B
including an awareness of leeway		C
• Techniques of visual fixing		B
• Use of GNSS and chart plotters for position fixing		B
• Use of waypoints to fix position		B
• Course to steer		B
11 Tides and Tidal Streams	4	
• Tidal definitions, levels and datum		B
• Tide tables		B
• Use of Admiralty method of determining tidal height at standard port		B
• Awareness of corrections for secondary ports		C
• Use of tidal diamonds and tidal stream atlases for chartwork		B
12 Visual Aids to Navigation	1	
• Lighthouses and beacons, light characteristics		B

	Minimum time (hours)	Depth of knowledge
13 Meteorology	3	
• Sources of broadcast meteorological information		B
• Knowledge of terms used in shipping forecasts, including the Beaufort Scale, and their significance to small craft		B
• Basic knowledge of highs, lows and fronts		C
14 Passage Planning	4	
• Preparation of a navigational plan for short coastal passages		C
• Meteorological considerations in planning short coastal passages		C
• Use of and visual confirmation of waypoints on passage		B
• Importance of confirmation of position by an independent source		A
• Keeping a navigational record		A
15 Navigation in Restricted Visibility	1	
• Precautions to be taken in, and limitations imposed by, fog		B
16 Pilotage	4	
• Use of transits, leading lines and clearing lines		B
• IALA system of buoyage (Regions A & B)		B
• Use of sailing directions		B
• Pilotage plans and harbour entry		B
17 Marine Environment	1	
• Responsibility for avoiding pollution and protecting the marine environment		B

RYA Coastal Skipper and Yachtmaster Offshore Theory Syllabus

This is an advanced course in navigation and meteorology for candidates for the RYA Coastal Skipper and Yachtmaster Offshore Shorebased Certificate.

The syllabus makes some provision for the revision of subjects in the Day Skipper Course, but those who have not acquired the knowledge set out in the Day Skipper Course are unlikely to be able to assimilate all the subjects covered in this advanced course in the time available.

The assumed level of knowledge before starting this course is the Day Skipper Shorebased Course.

Distance-learning students who intend to enter the MCA Large Yacht qualifications, such as Officer of the Watch or Master 3000, will require a formally invigilated exam. This exam will be conducted by an RYA Instructor or Examiner through an appropriately qualified RYA-recognised training centre.

	Minimum time (hours)	Depth of knowledge
1 Position	6	
• Dead reckoning and estimated position		B
• Satellite-derived position		A
• Use of waypoints to fix position		A
• Radar fixes		B
• Techniques of visual fixing		B
• Fixes using a mixture of position lines		B
• Relative accuracy of different methods of position fixing		A
• Areas of uncertainty		C
2 The Magnetic Compass	2	
• Allowance for variation		B
• Change of variation with time and position		B
• Causes of deviation		B
• Compass checks for deviation, but not correction		C
• Allowance for deviation		C
• Different types of compass		C
3 Tides	4	
• Causes of tides – springs and neaps		C
• Tide tables – sources		C
• Tidal levels and datum		B
• Standard and secondary ports		B
• Tidal anomalies (Solent, etc.)		C

	Minimum time (hours)	Depth of knowledge
4 Tidal Streams	3	
• Sources of tidal information		B
• Tidal stream information in sailing directions and yachtsmen's almanacs		B
• Allowance for tidal streams in computing a course to steer		A
• Tide rips, overfalls and races		B
• Tidal observation buoys, beacons etc.		B
5 Buoyage	1	
• IALA system buoyage in Regions A and B		B
• Limitations of buoys as navigational aids		C
6 Lights	1	
• Characteristics		B
• Ranges – visual, luminous and nominal		C
• Rising and dipping distances		C
• Light lists		C
7 Pilotage	3	
• Harbour regulations and control signals		A
• Methods of pre-planning		B
• Clearing lines		A
• Use of soundings		B
• Transits and leading lines		B
8 GNSS and Chart Plotters	3	
• Principles of operation and limitations of use		A
• Raster and vector charts		C
• Datum		C
• The importance of secondary means of position fixing via an independent source and keeping a separate record of position		A
• The importance of paper charts		B
9 Echo Sounders	0.5	
• Principles of operation and limitations of use		C

10 Logs (Speed and Distance Measuring)

Minimum time (hours): 0.5

- Principles of operation and limitations of use — C

11 Deck Log

Minimum time (hours): 0.5

- The importance of the log as a yacht's official document — B
- Layout of log, hourly and occasional entries — B

12 Meteorology

Minimum time (hours): 6

- Basic terms, the Beaufort Scale — B
- Air masses — B
- Cloud types — B
- Weather patterns associated with pressure and frontal systems — B
- Sources of weather forecasts — B
- Ability to interpret a shipping forecast, weatherfax and weather satellite information — B
- Land and sea breezes — B
- Sea fog — C
- Use of a barometer as a forecasting aid — B

13 Rules of the Road

Minimum time (hours): 1

- A sound knowledge of the International Regulations for Preventing Collisions at Sea, except Annexes 1 and 3 — A

14 Safety at Sea

Minimum time (hours): 2

- Personal safety, use of life jackets, safety harnesses and lifelines — B
- Fire prevention and firefighting — B
- Distress signals — B
- Coastguard and Boat Safety Scheme — C
- Preparation for heavy weather — B
- Life rafts and helicopter rescue — B
- Understanding of capabilities of vessel and basic knowledge of stability — B

	Minimum time (hours)	Depth of knowledge
15 Navigation in Restricted Visibility	1	
• Precautions to be taken in fog		B
• Limitations to safe navigation imposed by fog		B
• Navigation strategy in poor visibility		B
16 Passage Planning	5	
• Preparation of charts and notebook for route planning and for use on passage at sea		B
• Customs regulations as they apply to yachts		C
• Routine for navigating in coastal waters		B
• Strategy for course laying		B
• Use of and visual confirmation of waypoints and routes		A
• Use of weather forecast information for passage planning strategy		B
• Sources of local and national regulations		B
17 Marine Environment	0.5	
• The responsibility to minimise pollution and protect the marine environment		B

RYA Yachtmaster Ocean Theory Syllabus

This is a course in astro navigation and worldwide meteorology which also reveals the mysteries of the sextant. It assumes a sound knowledge of all subjects covered in the Day Skipper, and RYA Coastal Skipper and Yachtmaster Offshore Shorebased courses.

Minimum
time (hours)

1 The Earth and the Celestial Sphere   2

- The definition of observer's zenith and position of a heavenly body in terms of latitude, longitude, Greenwich Hour Angle (GHA) and declination
- Right angle relationships, latitude and co-latitude, declination and polar distance
- The relationship between GHA, longitude and Local Hour Angle (LHA)
- Tabulation of declination in nautical almanac
- The rate of increase of hour angle with time

2 The PZX Triangle   3

- The tabulated components of the triangle, LHA, co-latitude and polar distance
- The calculable components, zenith distance and azimuth
- The relationship between zenith distance and altitude
- Introduction to the tabular method of solution in the Air Navigation Tables and the basic sight form
- The use of calculators for the solution of the PZX triangle

3 The Sextant   2

- Practical guide to the use and care of a sextant at sea
- Conversion of sextant altitude to true altitude
- Application of dip, index error and refraction
- Correction of side error, perpendicularity, index error and collimation error

4 Measurement of Time   2

- Definition of, and relationship between, Universal Time (UT), Local Mean Time (LMT), standard time and zone time
- Rating of chronometers and watches

5 Meridian Altitudes   2

- Forecasting time of meridian altitude
- Reduction of meridian altitude sights

6 Sun, Star and other Sights

- Reduction and plotting of sun sights using Air Navigation Tables
- Awareness of use of a calculator for sight reduction
- The plotting of a sun-run-sun meridian altitude
- Awareness of the reduction and plotting of sights obtained from stars, moon and planets

7 Compass Checking
1

- Use of amplitude and azimuth tables systems and/or calculator

8 Satellite Navigation Systems
2

- Principles and limitations of use of all systems

9 Great Circle Sailing
1

- Comparison of rhumb lines and great circles
- Vertices and composite tracks
- The computation of a series of rhumb lines approximating to a great circle by use of gnomonic and Mercator projections

10 Meteorology
8

- General pressure distribution and prevailing winds over the oceans of the world
- Tropical revolving storms, seasonal occurrence and forecasting by observation

11 Passage Planning
7

- Publications available to assist with planning of long passages (routeing charts, ocean passages of the world and other publications)
- Preparation for ocean passage including survival equipment, victualling, water and fuel management, chafe protection, spares and maintenance

12 Passage-making
3

- Navigational routine
- Watchkeeping
- Crew management

13 Communications
2

- Satellite and terrestrial systems
- Weather information

One-day Shorebased Courses

The RYA offers a range of one-day courses which complement the Practical and navigation ones. Some are essential for those who wish to take examinations for their Certificates of Competence or work commercially as a skipper. For full details of the syllabus, please consult the RYA website www.rya.org.uk.

First Aid Syllabus

(Required for Commercial Endorsement)

In a medical emergency a little first aid knowledge and immediate action can save lives, especially in remote locations.

This one-day course is designed to provide a working knowledge of first aid for people using small craft and to support skippers of yachts and motor vessels. It fulfils the requirements for skippers of small craft working within 60 miles of a safe haven. The course is MCA and Health & Safety Executive (HSE) approved.

Duration: The minimum duration of the course is eight hours.

Pre-course knowledge: Nil.

Session 1

- Assessment, immediate actions and the priorities within first aid
- Unconsciousness and the recovery position
- CPR
- Drowning
- Breathing difficulties

Session 2

- Failure of the circulation; shock
- Blood loss and the control of bleeding
- Recognition of internal bleeding
- Angina and heart attack

Session 3

- Levels of response and the APVU scale
- Head injury: concussion and compression
- Immersion hypothermia and cold shock
- Burns, including sunburn
- Exposure hypothermia/hyperthermia
- Seasickness and dehydration
- Diabetic emergency
- Seizures

Session 4

- Fractures, including spinal injuries
- First aid kits
- Advice or assistance by radio
- Medivac: the evacuation of a casualty by helicopter

First Aid Syllabus

Session 5

For the skippers of MCA-coded boats:

- The contents and use of the category C first-aid kit, including the pocket mask

or

Subject of special interest to the group:

- Weil's disease; blue/green algae; child CPR; marine stings; fish hooks, etc.

Marine Radio (SRC) Syllabus

(Required for Commercial Endorsement)

The SRC (Short Range Certificate) course is for anyone who wishes to use fixed or handheld marine VHF radio. A radio is an important piece of safety equipment on board and it is vital to understand the correct procedures.

The Short Range Certificate is the minimum qualification required by law to control the operation of VHF and VHF Digital Selective Calling (DSC) equipment on any British-flagged vessel voluntarily fitted with a radio. This includes both fixed and hand-held equipment using international channels.

Course duration: The minimum duration for the classroom course is 10 hours of tuition (although 3 hours could be set as pre-work by the RYA Training Centre). Alternatively, an online interactive course is offered by many centres.

Examination: An independent examination will be conducted at an RYA Training Centre, consisting of a written and practical examination.

Pre-course knowledge: There is no mandatory pre-course knowledge. However, it is strongly recommended that candidates memorise the phonetic alphabet and read about distress messages prior to the course.

Course topics include:

- The basics of radio operation
- The correct frequencies (channels) to be used
- Distress, emergency and medical assistance procedures
- Making ship-to-shore telephone calls
- Digital Selective Calling (DSC) using simulators
- Global Maritime Distress and Safety System (GMDSS)
- Emergency Position Indicating Radio Beacons (EPIRB)
- Search and Rescue (SART)

Basic Sea Survival for Small Craft Syllabus

(Required for Commercial Endorsement)

The aim of the course is to give an understanding of how to use the safety equipment carried on small boats, including a practical session in launching and boarding a life raft.

The maximum number of students will be twice the life raft capacity (normally 12 to 16).

Course duration: The course duration is one day, including a two-hour practical session with a life raft in the water.

Pre-course knowledge: Nil.

1 Preparation for Sea Survival

- Survival difficulties
- Survival requirements
- Equipment available
- Actions prior to abandonment

2 Life Jackets and Life Rafts

Life jackets:

- Design and construction
- Correct donning procedure
- Purpose and use of life jackets

Safety harness:

- Purpose and use

Life rafts:

- Stowage and containment on board
- Types, design and construction
- Launching
- Abandoning the vessel and boarding the life raft
- Righting a capsized life raft
- Life raft equipment
- Initial actions to be taken in a life raft

3 Principles of Survival

- Methods to increase chances of survival
- Signs, symptoms and treatment of hypothermia
- Symptoms; method of treatment for sunburn, heat exhaustion and heatstroke
- Survival routines to aid location
- Correct use of pyrotechnics and other location aids
- Water rationing – procedures
- Dehydration and preventative measures
- Food rationing
- Sources of food

4 Survival-craft Ailments

5 Raft Management

6 Search and Rescue

- Rescue by helicopter or vessel
- The role of national Search and Rescue (SAR) organisations
- UK and international SAR organisations
- Other services

Diesel Engine Course Syllabus

The aim of the course is to give an awareness of the main systems of a marine diesel engine and the ability to take simple measures to prevent mechanical breakdown at sea and rectify defects which do not require workshop support.

Course duration: The minimum duration of the course is six hours.

A marine diesel engine (not necessarily in working condition) will be provided for practical sessions. No more than six students to one engine.

Pre-course knowledge: Nil.

1 Introduction
- Principles of the diesel engine

2 The Four-stroke Cycle
- Naturally aspirated engines
- Turbocharging
- Intercooling/aftercooling

3 The Fuel System
- The basic system
- The tank
- The water-separating pre-filter
- Fuel lift pump
- The engine fine filter
- Injection pump
- Injectors
- Bleeding the system

4 The Cooling System
- Seawater cooling
- Freshwater cooling
- Temperature control
- The thermostat
- The seawater impeller pump

5 The Air Systems
- The airway in
- The airway out

6 Engine Electrical Systems
- The basic system
- Battery capacity and care
- Drive belts
- The alternator

7 Spares and Tool Requirements
- Basic spares and tools

8 The Importance of Winterisation and Servicing
- Engine lubrication
- Transmission lubrication
- Winterisation and servicing
- Service schedule

9 Fault Finding

Radar Course Syllabus

This course gives you an understanding of radar as an aid to navigation and collision avoidance.

Cruising boats increasingly have radar on board. The International Regulations for Preventing Collisions at Sea require that if you have radar you must know how to use it.

Radar is probably the most versatile of all electronic navigation aids, but the best results are only obtained when you know how to use all the functions correctly. It is not an all-seeing eye, and can easily mislead those who do not understand its controls, allow for its limitations, or interpret its picture accurately.

Course duration: The course duration is one day.

Pre-course knowledge: Nil.

1 Basic understanding of Radar Wave Propagation
- Conditions giving rise to abnormal propagation

2 Radar Set Components
- Function and correct use of controls
- Correct setting-up procedure

3 Target Definition and Discrimination
- Spot size, pulse length and beam width
- Target characteristics, size, shape, material
- False echoes
- Shadow sectors, shadow diagram

4 Radar Reflectors
- Passive and active

World Sailing Offshore Safety Course

This course is primarily intended as training for recreational and racing skippers and crews who may encounter rough weather and problems at sea. This course, in conjunction with the RYA Basic Sea Survival course, meets the requirements of the World Sailing Offshore Special Regulations with regards to sea survival training for those involved in offshore races.

At the end of the course you will have a good knowledge of the safety equipment carried on small boats and the seamanship techniques needed to survive at sea in heavy weather.

Course duration: The World Sailing Offshore Safety course duration is one day.

For the purpose of satisfying the World Sailing Offshore Special Regulations, the candidates must update this training with an approved course every five years.

N.B.: The total duration of the combined RYA Basic Sea Survival course and World Sailing Offshore Safety course is two days.

Pre-course knowledge: Nil.

Course topics include:

*   One day of training in seamanship and emergencies, including heavy weather seamanship, weather forecasting, firefighting and man-overboard recovery

Professional Practices and Responsibilities Course

(Required for Commercial Endorsement)

A compulsory online course for RYA Commercial Endorsement holders.

Who this course is for: Whatever your job is on board, in the commercial world you are a professional seafarer. As such, you are no different from the captain of a cruise liner – you have a duty of care to crew, passengers, and other water users. This course will help you understand where to look up the information to stay safe and operate within the law.

The course is broken down into four modules:

* Commercial environment – how you fit into the professional maritime world
* People – the importance of correct manning, keeping your skills up to date and the safe management of commercial vessels
* Vessel – the compulsory carriage and maintenance of safety equipment, and how to create and implement risk control and operating procedures
* Purpose – making sure your vessel is suitable and legal for the work you are carrying out, your obligations in protecting the environment, appropriate planning, and situational awareness

Following the modules there is a practice assessment so you can check you are ready before moving on to the final graded online assessment.

We estimate users will take around six to eight hours to work through the four course modules. The graded end-of-course assessment is split into two sections, totalling two and a half hours.

How to take the Professional Practices and Responsibilities (PPR) Course

The PPR course is run by RYA Training Centres. Your RYA Training Centre will provide remote access to an Instructor who will be on hand to help if you have any queries during the online course.

Contact an RYA Training Centre or visit their website for more details.

You can take this course any time prior to your commercial endorsement application or renewal. Your PPR certificate will be valid either for your first Commercial Endorsement application or your next renewal.

The ICC (including the CEVNI Test)

Evidence of Competence Abroad

Many European countries require the skipper of a pleasure craft to be able to provide evidence of his or her competence. Experiences differ greatly. Inconsistency from province to province and port to port means many boaters are never asked to provide evidence of their competence abroad. However, those that are asked and do not have a suitable document can find themselves in an uncomfortable situation. This is where an ICC can prove to be useful.

The ICC

The ICC (or to give it its full title International Certificate for Operators of Pleasure Craft) is a certificate which is intended to provide evidence of competence when requested by officials in foreign countries. It is sometimes known as the International Certificate of Competence.

It is issued under the United Nations Economic Commission for Europe (UNECE) Inland Transport Committee Working Party on Inland Water Transport Resolution 40. It is this resolution which details how and to whom the ICC may be issued, the syllabus requirements, the layout of the certificate and it also lists the countries which have notified the UNECE Secretariat that they have accepted the resolution.

So what does the ICC do?

When you visit another country, in most circumstances (in accordance with the United Nations Convention on the Law of the Sea) you can be required to comply with the maritime legislation of the visited country (the Coastal State) in addition to that of your vessel's country of registration (Flag State).

The regulations for pleasure craft can vary considerably from one country to another and the regime for skipper training and licensing can be equally disparate; the ICC helps to overcome the difficulties these differences can cause.

An ICC issued by a contracting Government to Resolution 40 indicates that the certificate holder has demonstrated the level of competence required by Resolution 40 for the certificate to be issued. In other words it is an assurance from one Government to another that the certificate holder is sufficiently competent to be driving a pleasure craft, despite not holding the visited country's national certificate.

Formal Acceptance of the ICC

The ICC should be automatically accepted in countries which have adopted Resolution 40. However of the 56 UNECE countries, able to accept the resolution the UK is one of only a handful which have fully adopted Resolution 40. Many of the eligible countries have not accepted Resolution 40, some still apply Resolution 14 which Resolution 40 was intended to replace and others only apply Resolution 40 in part or with caveats attached.

Wider (Informal) Acceptance

The ICC is however a far more useful document than the Resolution's formal acceptance would suggest. Although acceptance of the ICC by the visited country should be because the visited country itself has adopted Resolution 40, the ICC is sometimes recognised as an acceptable certificate in the visited country's national legislation and is quite often accepted on a purely informal basis. Spain, Greece and Portugal, for example, have not adopted Resolution 40 but are still likely to ask visitors for an ICC.

The ICC may be acceptable for visiting foreign flagged vessels, foreign flagged vessels being kept in the Coastal State and/or vessels flagged in the Coastal State. It should never be assumed that the ICC will be accepted as an alternative to the national qualification of the vessel's flag state. The onus is on ICC holders to determine its acceptability by foreign states, as the ICC was never intended to be an alternative to individual national qualification requirements.

Further information about where the RYA recommends having an ICC can be found at www.rya.org.uk/go/eoca.

Who can get an ICC from the RYA?

The RYA is authorised by the Maritime and Coastguard Agency (MCA) to issue the ICC, on behalf of the UK Government, to qualifying individuals. Applicants for the RYA ICC must be eligible to be issued the certificate and must demonstrate the necessary knowledge and skills.

Eligibility

The certificate is available to a person who fulfils the following eligibility criteria:

- has reached the age of 16
- is physically and mentally fit to operate a pleasure craft, and in particular, has sufficient powers of vision and hearing
- presents one of the specified UK certificates or has successfully passed an examination to prove the necessary competence for pleasure craft operation
- who presents evidence of nationality or residency to show that their nationality does not precluded them from being issued with an ICC by the RYA

Evidence of Nationality or Residency

The RYA is authorised by the Maritime and Coastguard Agency (MCA) to issue a UK ICC to the nationals of any country EXCEPT individuals who are a national of another UNECE member state which has accepted Resolution 40 and who are also resident in another UNECE member state which has accepted Resolution 40, unless the RYA has been given written permission to do so by the Government of the relevant country.

The list of UNECE member states that have accepted Resolution 40 is subject to change without notice (i.e. whenever the government of a country adopts Resolution 40). The current list is available on the RYA web-site at www.rya.org.uk/go/icc-no.

A person's eligibility can therefore change during the period the ICC is valid for. Should this be the case, the certificate holder must notify the RYA and surrender the certificate; no refunds of any nature will be given. If the certificate holder cannot satisfactorily demonstrate his or her continued eligibility when the certificate expires it will not be renewed by the RYA.

Applicants are required to provide evidence of their eligibility when they first apply for an ICC and must provide evidence that they remain eligible to be issued with the ICC on renewal.

An individual who is not eligible to be issued with an ICC by the RYA (by virtue of their nationality and place of residence) should be able to obtain an ICC from their own Government. They must however note that possession of an RYA certificate does not entitle them to a certificate issued by any other organisation or on behalf of any other national Government.

Individuals with dual nationality may apply for the UK ICC issued by the RYA if either nationality makes them eligible to do so. It should however be noted that only the nationality which made the individual eligible for the certificate to be issued will be recorded on the ICC.

Demonstrating the Necessary Knowledge and Skills

Resolution 40 requires that applicants for the ICC prove that they have sufficient knowledge and ability to safely operate a pleasure craft. This can be done by presenting a recognised national certificate issued by the country which is issuing the ICC. Alternatively the Resolution makes provision for boater to pass an examination.

The UK ICC, issued by the RYA, has five categories: Inland Waters, Coastal Waters, Power, Sail and Personal Watercraft. When an ICC is issued, only the categories for which competence has been demonstrated will be validated.

If you have already passed an RYA practical course, your course completion certificate or Certificate of Competence may help you to obtain an ICC.

Experienced skippers can also qualify for the ICC by successfully completing an assessment of their competence through an RYA recognised training centre or an affiliated club authorised to carry out the assessment, rather than having to attend a full RYA training course. The syllabus for the ICC assessment is detailed on the ICC application form, which is available from the RYA website (www.rya.org.uk/go/iccform).

For more information on how to apply for the ICC, please visit www.rya.org.uk/go/iccapply.

Applying for your First ICC

To obtain an ICC, you must complete an ICC Application Form in full and sign the declaration.

This should be sent to the RYA Certification Department, together with:

* a passport sized photograph (with your name on the reverse)
* proof that your nationality or your country of residence make you eligible to be issued with a UK ICC issued by the RYA
* evidence of your competence (relevant sections of the application form have been signed to say you have passed the ICC assessment or the ICC CEVNI Test or photocopies of any certificates you are presenting as evidence are enclosed
* payment (including the fast track fee if required) – the ICC is issued to RYA Members free of charge

Renewing an ICC

The ICC is valid for five years.

Unless you wish to have additional categories added to your ICC, the renewal process is simply a paper exercise.

Boating Inland and CEVNI

Code Européen des Voies de Navigation Intérieure (CEVNI) is the code governing navigation on the interconnected European inland waterways and is the basis of many of the various countries' own regulations.

Signs, rules and procedures for navigating many of the European inland waterways are all included within CEVNI and in the same way as pleasure craft on coastal waters are expected to abide by the COLREGS, pleasure craft on many of the inland waterways of Europe, which in places are heavily utilised by commercial traffic, are expected to know and follow CEVNI.

Resolution 40 requires that candidates applying for an ICC with the inland category validated have sufficient knowledge of the traffic regulations applicable on inland waters, in particular CEVNI. CEVNI is not covered in any of the RYA's courses, even those specific to inland waterways, as these regulations are not in use in the UK. It is therefore necessary to have a separate theory test on the CEVNI regulations.

There is however no separate CEVNI certificate or CEVNI endorsement. Passing the CEVNI Test simply allows the Inland category on your ICC to be validated, thereby indicating that you have demonstrated knowledge of the CEVNI regulations as required by the Resolution.

All candidates requiring the inland category validated must pass the ICC CEVNI Test irrespective of whether the CEVNI regulations are in force in the country or on the river, lake or canal where they intend to go boating.

The ICC CEVNI Test

You can arrange to take the ICC CEVNI Test through RYA recognised training centres and affiliated clubs that are authorised to carry out the test.

The RYA ICC CEVNI test is a multiple choice paper. Costs for the CEVNI test will vary between organisations (RYA recognised training centres and RYA affiliated clubs).

There are two options:

• Take the test in person at an RYA recognised training centre or an affiliated club authorised to carry out the test; or

• Many RYA recognised training centres or affiliated clubs authorised to carry out the test can provide you with access to take the test online remotely from home or anywhere in the world

The publication *RYA European Waterways Regulations* (G17) provides the information you need to learn the code in a clear and concise way – a sample paper can be found at the back of the book.

In addition to passing the CEVNI test, for an ICC to be issued you must present a qualifying RYA practical course completion certificate or pass an ICC assessment at an RYA recognised training centre and be eligible to be issued with an ICC.

To find out more about the ICC CEVNI test, please visit www.rya.org.uk/go/cevnitest.

For further information on the ICC, please visit www.rya.org.uk/go/icc.

Recorded Achievement

You can keep a record of your achievements by attaching your course completion certificates in the following pages. It is important to keep your logbook and certificates in a safe place as the RYA keeps a central record of only course completion certificates relating to 'command qualifications', such as Day Skipper and Coastal Skipper Practical courses.

Please note the difference between course completion certificates and Certificates of Competence.

Translations

Most of the Practical certificates have been translated into several languages. They are available from the RYA website www.rya.org.uk.

Certificates of Competence

RYA/MCA Yachtmaster Coastal and RYA Yachtmaster Offshore Certificates of Competence are only awarded after the successful completion of a practical examination at sea with an RYA/MCA-appointed Examiner who is independent of the school with which you have trained.

RYA/MCA Yachtmaster Ocean Certificates of Competence are awarded to holders of RYA/MCA Yachtmaster Offshore Certificates of Competence who have successfully completed the required ocean qualifying passage and successfully pass an oral assessment.

The RYA maintains a record of holders of RYA/MCA Certificates of Competence.

Course Completion Certificates

The authority to award certificates of satisfactory completion of Practical courses is delegated to RYA Training Centres, which may be clubs, sailing schools or sea-training organisations.

Individual Instructors not working as part of a recognised centre may not run courses, sign the course sections of the logbook, or issue certificates. If in doubt about whether a particular RYA Training Centre holds valid RYA Training recognition status, please check the RYA website for a full list of RYA Training Centres or contact RYA Training for verification.

Own-boat Tuition

RYA Training Centres may offer instruction for RYA certificates in a student's boat. Before doing so, the Principal will ensure that the boat is in sound condition and is adequately equipped both for safety and effective instruction.

Course Completion Certificates

Sailing Skills: Start Sailing Level 1

ATTACH YOUR CERTIFICATE HERE

Sailing Skills: Start Sailing Level 2

ATTACH YOUR CERTIFICATE HERE

Start Yachting

ATTACH YOUR CERTIFICATE HERE

Start Motor Cruising

ATTACH YOUR CERTIFICATE HERE

Helmsman's Course

ATTACH YOUR CERTIFICATE HERE

Competent Crew

ATTACH YOUR CERTIFICATE HERE

Watch Leader

ATTACH YOUR CERTIFICATE HERE

Day Skipper

Qualification ..**Day Skipper**...

Date ....

Training Centre ....

Instructor's Name ....

Certificate Number ....

Advanced Pilotage

ATTACH YOUR CERTIFICATE HERE

Coastal Skipper

Qualification ..**Coastal Skipper**...

Date ....

Training Centre ....

Instructor's Name ....

Certificate Number ....

Essential Navigation and Seamanship

ATTACH YOUR CERTIFICATE HERE

Day Skipper Shorebased

ATTACH YOUR CERTIFICATE HERE

RYA Coastal Skipper and Yachtmaster Offshore Theory

ATTACH YOUR CERTIFICATE HERE

RYA Yachtmaster Ocean Theory

ATTACH YOUR CERTIFICATE HERE

First Aid

ATTACH YOUR CERTIFICATE HERE

Marine Radio (SRC)

Qualification ..**Marine Radio (SRC)**...

Date ....

Training Centre ....

Instructor's Name ....

Assessor's Name ....

115

Basic Sea Survival for Small Craft

ATTACH YOUR CERTIFICATE HERE

Diesel Engine

ATTACH YOUR CERTIFICATE HERE

Radar

ATTACH YOUR CERTIFICATE HERE

World Sailing Offshore Safety

ATTACH YOUR CERTIFICATE HERE

Professional Practices and Responsibilities

Qualification ..**Professional Practices and Responsibilities**...

Date ....

Training Centre ....

Instructor Pathway

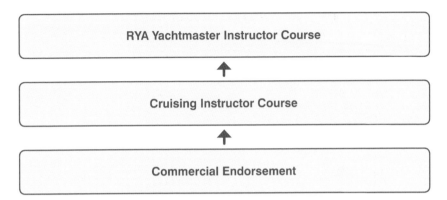

To be successful in any of the Instructor courses candidates must have a high level of subject knowledge. For instance, it would be unlikely that a newly qualified RYA Yachtmaster Offshore would pass a Cruising Instructor course unless already an Instructor in another discipline, and having a very good depth of knowledge. Similarly, a Cruising Instructor applying for an RYA Yachtmaster Instructor course must have gained experience at Cruising Instructor level before attempting to progress.

More details of prerequisites can be found on the RYA website (www.rya.org.uk).

Procedure for Appeal against the Outcome of an RYA Course or Examination

Assessment Standards

All RYA-qualified Instructors, Assessors, Trainers and Examiners are required to treat students and candidates with respect and fairness.

All assessments in the use of boats and their equipment have implications for the safety of life at sea. It is therefore essential that candidates are given a thorough and searching assessment. It would be dangerous to the candidate and anyone with whom he or she subsequently goes to sea if an Instructor, Examiner or Assessor erred on the side of leniency in awarding a certificate. There must never be any question of relaxing the standards required for an award.

Realistic Aims

In many cases it becomes clear to the Instructor, Examiner or Assessor at an early stage in the assessment process that the candidate has been over-ambitious in their choice of course or award. In such instances the Assessor should discuss the situation with the candidate and agree revised aims which are achievable within the time frame of the course or examination.

In the case of examinations for Certificates of Competence, where it becomes obvious to the Examiner shortly after the commencement of the exam that the candidate is not to the required standard, the Examiner may be able to offer an exam for a lower level of Certificate of Competence. Generally speaking, however, a candidate will be examined for the qualification for which they have applied and will receive either a pass or fail recommendation from the Examiner.

Grounds for Appeal

A candidate has grounds for appeal if he or she believes either:

- That they have not been given a reasonable opportunity to demonstrate their competence, or
- That they have been placed under undue or unfair pressure by the person carrying out the assessment.

Appeals against Assessment at an RYA Training Centre

The appeal should be stated to the Principal of the training centre. The Principal should discuss the appeal with the Instructor concerned and, if appropriate, with other Instructors who have witnessed the assessment. The Principal should then either inform the appellant that the assessment has been fairly and correctly carried out, or arrange for another assessment to be carried out by a different Assessor.

If the appellant is dissatisfied with the decision of the Principal, he or she may appeal in writing to the RYA Chief Instructor for the relevant scheme, care of RYA Head Office in Hamble, U.K. The Chief Instructor for the scheme will consult with those carrying out the original assessment and any witnesses to the assessment. They will then decide whether or not a further assessment should be made. Where appropriate, the matter will be referred to the RYA Training Manager.

Appeal against the Result of an RYA/MCA Examination

The appellant should make an appeal, in writing, to the RYA Chief Examiner.

The Chief Examiner will contact the Examiner making the assessment and any competent witness to the assessment process. The Chief Examiner will then decide whether the applicant should be offered a reassessment by another Examiner or whether the result of the original examination should stand. Where appropriate, the matter will be referred to the RYA/MCA Yachtmaster Qualification Panel.

The outcome of appeals decided by the RYA Chief Examiner will be reported to the RYA/MCA Yachtmaster Qualification Panel.

Notes

Shop online at
www.rya.org.uk/shop

- Secure online ordering
- 15% discount for RYA members
- Books, DVDs, navigation aids and lots more
- Free delivery to a UK address for RYA members on orders over £25
- Free delivery to an overseas address for RYA members on orders over £50
- Buying online from the RYA shop enables the RYA in its work on behalf of its members